DWARVES WAR-FIGHTING MANUAL

Also by Den Patrick:

Orcs War-Fighting Manual
Elves War-Fighting Manual

ᚦWARVES

WAR-FIGHTING MANUAL

Den Patrick

Illustrations by Andrew James

Den Patrick (signature)

A James (signature)

GOLLANCZ
LONDON

The right of Den Patrick to be identified
as the author of this work has been asserted by him in
accordance with the Copyright, Designs and Patents Act 1988.

First published in Great Britain in 2013 by Gollancz
An imprint of the Orion Publishing Group
Orion House, 5 Upper St Martin's Lane, London WC2H 9EA
An Hachette UK Company

A CIP catalogue record for this book is available
from the British Library

ISBN 978 0 575 13279 5

1 3 5 7 9 10 8 6 4 2

Typeset at The Spartan Press Ltd,
Lymington, Hants

Printed and bound in Great Britain by
Clays Ltd, St Ives plc

The Orion Publishing Group's policy is to use papers that
are natural, renewable and recyclable products and made
from wood grown in sustainable forests. The logging and
manufacturing processes are expected to conform to the
environmental regulations of the country of origin.

www.orionbooks.co.uk
www.gollancz.co.uk

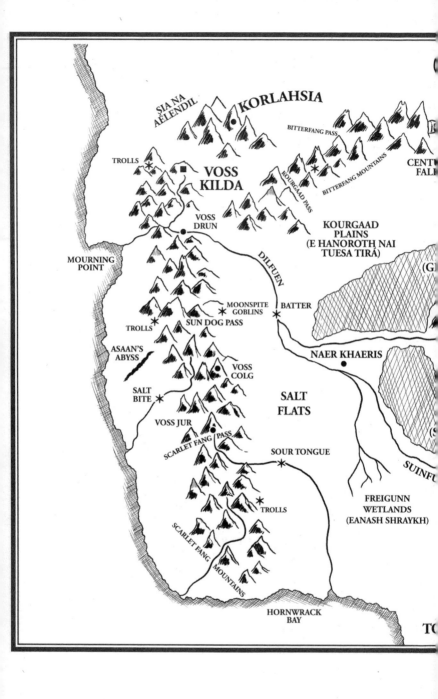

The Dwarven
Field Manual

1

An Introduction

*'It's not the size of the dwarf in the fight,
it's the size of the fight in the dwarf.'*

Striden-dirigent Sundin Hallestøm in conversation
during the Tomb Blight infestation of Voss Kilda.

Subjugation of the Dvergiir[1]

We dwarves are not a race that bears the yoke of
subjugation kindly. We were created by the Great
Drakes themselves, who had little use for us but as

1 *Dvergiir* is how the dwarves refer to themselves, and likely the root of the
human word in both the Arend Kingdom and Hoim. It is likely the Arends
would have omitted the 'iir', simply calling them 'dverg', which changed
over time to its current form. The dwarves, who enjoy shortening words
informally, have come to use both terms and this is reflected in the translation.

slaves.[2] We suffered for centuries, toiling in the mines, gathering great wealth for our masters, until Odniir Dwarf-Father led the rebellion.[3] That rebellion should not define us. Let it not be said that we are untrustworthy and treacherous. This is not so.

Odniir, who at that time was called Longbeard, was summoned in the dead of night to the hall of Brutenmakt.

2 The dwarves maintain that the Great Drakes slumber beneath the earth in cavernous halls, abed piles of gold and trinkets. I would think it fodder for a children's story if not for the fact that the elves speak of *draekaoin*. Even the no-nonsense orcs speak of *daginn*. I can only conclude dragons are real. I hope they sleep on, undisturbed. Brutenmakt himself is rumoured to sleep under a mountain near Kourgaad Pass.

3 Odniir Longbeard, later called Odniir Dwarf-Father, is the most famous of all dwarves. The dwarves revere no gods, and are at odds with their creators, the Great Drakes. It is for this reason they have turned to the worship of their ancestors and seek to beatify the bravest and wisest of their kin.

The ancient drake had caught five dwarves attempting to steal a golden ring, inlaid with diamonds and other pale stones, which to dwarves was the size of a crown.

Odniir was dismayed, asking the dwarves why they had embarked on such a foolhardy endeavour. The dwarves replied that their families were starving; they had hoped to sell the crown to some elves, who possessed an abundance of food. Brutenmakt raged and declared the thieves must be put to death, but Odniir stood his ground and sent for their families. He took the golden crown from the starving dwarves and offered it back to Brutenmakt, but, in a fit of pique, the Great Drake declined to accept the stolen treasure.

Hollow-eyed and emaciated dwarves slowly assembled in the lofty hall of Brutenmakt. It had been a long time since any of them had enjoyed enough to eat. Odniir presented the families to Brutenmakt and attempted to reason with the ancient drake, but their creator would not be appeased. He was incensed at the attempt on the ring. In a rage he turned on the thieves and their families, consuming all in one fiery breath.

Odniir looked upon the smouldering corpses of his kin in horror. A terrible frown creased his brow. He had been working through the night, helping some miners, when he had been summoned by his master. The stolen treasure weighed heavy in his hand, lent awful significance by the brutal deaths of those now reduced to ash. Odniir placed the crown on his head and shouted defiantly, 'Regard, Brutenmakt! I have your trinket now. Would you destroy me in so callous a fashion?'

And Brutenmakt did that very thing: he breathed in

and the fires of his hatred lit the hall as bright as day. The crown, however, flared into life with a cool blue light that shielded the dwarf from the hungry flames.[4] Brutenmakt could not understand how the dwarf remained, and looked on aghast. It was in this moment that Odniir stepped up to his master, and, using his miner's sledgehammer, rendered the Great Drake unconscious. It is said Odniir struck Brutenmakt so hard a quake overtook the land. The *huldurfolka* woke from their slumber, snow was shaken from mountaintops along the Bitterfangs, and the elves cowered beneath the trees as the land trembled. Even the orcs were troubled, and retreated to seek counsel from their shamans. This single hammer strike marked the beginning of the rebellion, and a change in the fortunes of dwarves everywhere.

Odniir led his people to freedom, and they named him Dwarf-Father. In time he freed all dwarves, and none remained in thrall to the Great Drakes.

A NEW ENEMY

The newly freed dwarves founded secluded settlements in the mountains, which we love more than life itself. It was from here the goblins attempted to cast us out, but their every attempt failed. We were watched over by mighty *huldurfolka*, who themselves knew all too well

4 There are examples throughout dwarf folklore of large creatures making rings, which end up as belts or crowns for the dwarves. This particular crown is called the Kall Krona, the Cold Crown, and is worn by the King of Voss Kilda to this day.

the callous nature of the Great Drakes.[5] The goblins, having long inhabited the mountains, remain our constant companions: thornier than any gorse, predictable as the rising of the sun, and as devious as the Ruiirmaidens.[6] Their efforts to dislodge us are for naught. We dwarves endure and turn back their assaults, cleaving thieving fingers from dirty hands, telling many a joke about the fidelity of their mothers. As the years passed, our settlements grew, surrounded by stout walls, guarded by the brave.

STORGUNN AND The ELVES

The elves, while not so stupid as to try to remove us from our homes, have conspired to thwart our progress. At first they were simply content to turn Storgunn against

5 *Huldurfolka* are better known as golems to humans. They are beings of living stone nearly thirty feet tall. The dwarves maintain the golems were created by the Great Drakes to serve as builders. It is the *huldurfolka* who built the halls of the drakes, but their creators soon tired of them and cast them out. The golems live under mountains and near waterfalls, in deep communion with the land. Their name means 'hidden folk'. They have an uncanny ability to remain undetected, despite their tremendous size.

6 The Ruiirmaidens are sometimes called norns. They appear in many tales as a trio of beautiful but capricious women. They have the Sight, and are sought out by many a great warrior wanting to know what destiny awaits him. The Ruiirmaidens appear differently in each tale, sometimes being a mother, maiden and crone; other times three witches attended by a host of ravens. Yet other tales speak of elfin beauties who enchant and seduce. I lived nine long months with the dwarves and could well have used the company of the Ruiirmaidens in that last aspect.

us with honeyed lies and pretty misdirection.[7] The star of the West declined to teach our kin the ways of root and leaf, and the many sciences of growing things. While we can draw strength from the land, our longevity is as nothing compared to the infinite span of an elf. Dwarves can live for three centuries, rarely longer.

The elves were much changed after Storgunn returned to her place among the stars. They had become arrogant and introspective and harboured little interest in trading with us. Once again the dwarves faced starvation. Then, salting the wound, the elves slew Killi Berigunn, son of Berigunn the Furious, Storvaldr of beloved Voss Kilda. This event alone precipitated a war of eighty years with the hated *bikkja*.[8] Trust not those capricious and unruly beings. They think themselves above the concerns of mortals and are to be despised.

7 Storgunn, meaning 'royal star', is the name the dwarves give to the divine being the elves call Khaeris. While the dwarves accept her divine nature in a casual fashion, they do not worship her. Many dwarves feel they were duped out of the better part of Storgunn's teachings by the elves, who always enjoyed her favour. This has created much sourness in the dwarf spirit, and is something they like to complain about at length. And when I say 'at length' I mean, for seven nights in succession. The only defence to this orgy of self-pity was to get completely hammered on the fine ale of my hosts.

8 *Bikkja* is the *dvergiir* word for dog or wolf, specifically the bitches. It is also the common derogatory name dwarves use for elves, specifically the male elves. *Bikkja* is also the word the Arends use for their dogs. As a consequence of terming the elves, whom the dwarves deem whiny, *bikkja*, the term 'bitching' is applied to any complaint or protracted gripe.

the golden age of the dwarves

Storgunn had taught ten dwarves the mastery of stone and instructed them in the finer points of metallurgy. These ten dwarves each took nine apprentices and journeyed home to the dwarven settlements, whereupon they fashioned great halls beneath the ground for their kin.[9] The dwarves spent the next thousand years reclaiming their subterranean heritage. Vast citadels were built beneath the mountains rivalling the halls of the Great Drakes. The goblins despaired. We were more entrenched than ever, and our excavations had uncovered bright seams of gold and veins of strong metals. New weapons were fashioned, hastening the demise of the green-skinned devils. The populations of our cities swelled.

the vaetiir – unwelcome companions

Even the ten industrious centuries of our Golden Age knew little peace. Strange and malicious water spirits attacked lone travellers, making a nuisance of themselves near our building sites. Supplies of food and wood were led astray by the glamours and *ginning* of the *vaetiir*.[10] Some of these capricious sprites dared to intrude into the

9 Note how the ten experts took nine apprentices each, making their total number one hundred. The dwarves are deeply fond of this number, and it crops up time and again in their culture.

10 *Ginning* – the literal translation means 'deluding', which is also the dwarf word for magic. The dwarves seem confused on this issue; the line between the illusions of the *vaetiir* and the magic of the elves is a blurred one.

lower levels of our citadels. The more we built, the more the *vaetiir* sought to befuddle and confound. The longer we remained, the more devious the spirits became. *Ruszalkai* and *Vodyniir* sought to make safe passage from the citadels a distant memory.

And then came the tomb blights. But these are best left for another time, when the terror of the tale may be truly told. It could be that the *vaetiir*, *nockiir*, tomb blights and goblins (who never ceased their attacks) kept the fighting spirit of the dwarves alive.[11]

The Gift of Distrust

So it is that we dwarves can rely on nothing. Our creators are callous and cruel, our enemies many, and those who should be allies are untrustworthy dogs. Even the beneficent Storgunn turned her face from us. Only the strength, loyalty and duty of the dwarves can enable us to endure in such a hostile world. Only our fortifications, armour and weapons give us hope. Only distrust, suspicion and vigilance can protect us in the years to come.

This manual lays out the basic tenets of dwarven military strategy. The following chapters describe how

---

11 The *nockiir* of the dwarves are better known to humans, the Arends especially, as knuckers – terrible water serpents that frequently reach twenty feet long. My mother often warned me that one would come for me in the night if I were not a well-behaved little boy. I can only conclude my life has been less than virtuous as I was attacked by these savage creatures no less than three times during my nine-month stay with the dwarves. I must mend my ways, it seems.

we serve, whom we fight and what is expected of every dwarf of fighting age.[12]

The Dwarven Field Manual is the essential handbook for every soldier, every *Århundrade*, every dwarf in every citadel.[13] Here, set down in no-nonsense language, lie our tactics, the equipment we use to defeat the enemy, and the weapons at our disposal. It is the distilled wisdom of everything we have ever fought for and every conflict we have endured.

Read closely and may your beard grow long,

Striden-dirigent Sundin Hallestøm[14]

---

12 The definition of 'fighting age' is never discussed in dwarf culture. From my perspective, 'fighting age' seems to span from the time a dwarf can lift a pickaxe to the time that dwarf is found dead on a pile of goblin corpses. Details vary, but not much.

13 *Århundrade* means century, both in terms of a period of years and as a number. It is also the word given to a company of fighting dwarves. This is discussed in more detail in Chapter 2: Organisation of the Dwarves.

14 Often truncated to '*dirigent*', leader of a squad of twenty dwarves. Equivalent to a sergeant in our own army. The dwarf word *dirigent* is likely the root of 'diligent' among the Arends, and for good reason. *Striden-dirigents* and *Sektion-dirigents* are also covered in Chapter 2: Organisation of the Dwarves.

2

ORGANISATION OF the DWARVES

'The trouble with you humans is that you couldn't get shit-faced in a brewery. You lack the will. The will and the organisation.'

Striden-dirigent Sundin Hallestøm
in conversation at Storvaldrfest.

Dwarven society is based on the ideal that all dwarves know their place, seeking only to serve their king and citadel to the best of their ability. When the time comes to take action, there is no indecision, no pointless debate, no arguing. Our efficiency stems from this discipline and our results flourish from old-fashioned obedience. This is how dwarven lives are lived every day in citadels across Nedanförvärld.

In wartime, this principle is observed with even greater zeal, and it is this discipline that sets us apart from the other races. The elves are undoubtedly torn between taking up arms or composing pointless songs and poetry; the orcs' belligerence inevitably turns inward so that they fight among their own. A *dvergiir* is not weighed down by flaws of ego or bloodlust; he is free to serve our king, and in so doing provides service to his fellow dwarves, and ultimately himself.

ÐVERGÏÏR

Each dwarf in the company is outfitted with padded leather armour and a full suit of mail. This makes the business of preparing for war a costly one for any citadel treasury. A helmet is given to each dwarf when he reaches his twentieth year, usually by his family. Weapons are provided by the citadel, unless the dwarf has bought his own. Most warriors do not own crossbows and these are almost exclusively the property of the citadel. By contrast, dwarves wielding hammers take it as a point of honour to have a personalised weapon. These warriors record their kills as notches along the shaft. A *dvergiir* begins service using a crossbow before 'moving up' to close-quarters weaponry.[1] Dwarves are rarely full-time soldiers, and usually spend much of the week about their main job. One day of every week is given over to training, which will be overseen by the *Striden-dirigent*.

1 It is an endearing quality of these curt and irascible people that they deploy their youngest warriors at the rear, bearing ranged weapons. I suspect this tradition stems from when the dwarf population was much smaller and threatened with extinction. Young dwarves were, and still are, greatly treasured, even if they do 'only have short beards and can't drink to save their lives, much less their mothers'.'

ÅRḢUNÐRAÐE

The *Århundrade* is a company of dwarves one hundred strong, or so the *Stridenvaldr*[2] would have everyone believe. Every *Århundrade* leaves a symbolic ten warriors at the citadel to act as a garrison to protect the young, reducing the company to ninety. Factor in casualties (either from mining or war) and a further twenty to thirty dwarves can be accounted for. It is rare in the extreme that an *Århundrade* features its full complement of one hundred warriors.[3] Tales of 'one hundred dwarves, loyal and true' are exactly that, just tales.

CRUPP

The *Århundrade* is divided into five *trupp*, consisting of nineteen warriors led by a *Striden-dirigent*. Each soldier in the *trupp* will sport the company colour on his right pauldron, often dyeing the leather grip of his weapon the same colour. *Trupp* are organised by weapon type and there are four distinct squads: hammers (*näven*), axes (*talongen*), spears (*törne*) and crossbows (*huggtand*).

All dwarves begin their fighting years in a *huggtand*. It is only after they have survived a decade's worth of

2 *Stridenvaldr* – equivalent to lieutenant in our own armies. *Stridenvaldr* are often ambitious nobles' sons, keen to make a name for themselves, seeking promotion to *Kull*. It was my opinion they are not well liked.

3 The dwarves have no word for 'warrior'; it is implied and expected that each dwarf be able to fight. There are relatively few career soldiers and all dwarves form a highly trained militia. It is for this reason that the dwarves can mobilise so much of their population. I have used the word 'warrior' in this translation to avoid confusion among human readers.

engagements that they can request to join a *näven-trupp*, *törne-trupp* or *talongen-trupp*.

KULL

Each citadel has two *Hertig*, one for the north and one for the south.[4] They are entrusted to look after the safety of the halls in their region, patrol the surrounding caves, and set guards at every gate and entrance. The *Hertig* are the highest-ranking nobles below the king, and each has a number of *Kull* who swear oaths of loyalty to him. In small citadels *Kull* might only be two or three in number. A *Kull* is responsible for leading an *Århundrade*. His official title is *Stor-striden*, but it is easier to shout '*Kull*' on the battlefield. Given the choice between a military rank and one of birth, dwarves inevitably choose to address a leader by his title. Dwarves are a traditional lot, and given to fawning over their 'betters'. A career soldier who somehow rises to lead an *Århundrade* without noble blood will be addressed as *Stor-striden*, just to remind him of his low birth.[5] It would be better for

4 *Hertig* are the proudest and most stubborn dwarves, deeply impressed with their own lineage and given to long rambling tales about the honour of their family. *Hertig* are akin to human rank of duke, but even our dukes would struggle to compete with the pomp of their dwarven equivalents.

5 The dwarves have turned distrust into an art form only surpassed by their ability to heap disdain on everyone else. To this end they have invented a class system. The lower class are miners and front-line soldiers; the middle class are artisans and merchants; and the upper class, or *valdr*, are nobility. It seems to me the class system was created so that dwarves could discriminate against each other when there was a lack of elves or humans present. The dwarves reserve the greatest part of their scorn for merchants, who are particularly wealthy but lack lineage. They are termed *ny-valdr*, meaning 'newly rich'.

14

all if this particular dwarf tradition were to fall off a mountain.[6]

STRIDEN-DIRIGENT

The *Striden-dirigent* is appointed by the *Kull* and commands nineteen dwarves, together forming a *trupp*. The *dirigent* is a full-time member of the citadel army and his sole responsibility is the training, upkeep and welfare of his men. All *dirigent* are expected to be masters of hammer, axe, crossbow and spear.

Some *dirigent* choose to divide the *trupp* into two more manageable parts called *sektions*. This is more useful if the *trupp* has been entrusted to defend a large area, or needs to send word to another part of the citadel. This smaller unit of soldiers are led by a *Sektion-dirigent*, who will be a trusted veteran of the *trupp*.

HOJTA-DIRIGENT

The *Hojta-dirigent*, often just '*Hojta*' or simply '*Hoj*', is a rank above *Striden-dirigent* but below the command rank of *Stridenvaldr*. The *Hoj* is responsible first and foremost for the discipline of the *Århundrade*. It is for this reason a *Hoj* will have the loudest voice and be implacable and intimidating in equal measure. The *Hoj*, while not liked, is respected. He ensures the *Striden-dirigent* are performing their tasks properly, but also

6 'Fall off a mountain' is a figure of speech not unlike 'fall by the wayside'. Being a dwarven disparagment, this is always said with a good deal of bile and sounds distinctly more permanent than its human equivalent.

serves as an intermediary to the command ranks. The *Hoj* is perhaps the most difficult role in the *Århundrade*, attracting a particular type of hoary and stern-faced dwarf.

STRIÐENVALÐR

There are two or three *Stridenvaldr* attached to every *Århundrade*. They assist the *Kull* in leading the company and maintaining discipline. They are often sent to relay orders and restore flagging morale. A *trupp* can be led by a *Stridenvaldr* if the mission requires it, although this is generally avoided. These officers are appointed by the *Kull* from candidates put forward by the *Ragnvaldr*,[7] often descended from families with long and glorious histories. *Stridenvaldr* are traditionally accompanied by two bodyguards that are not officially part of the *Århundrade*; their priority is to keep the *Stridenvaldr* alive and out of enemy hands.[8] These bodyguards can't be trusted

---

7 The *Ragnvaldr* are seven dwarves who serve on the ruling council of each citadel. They serve at the king's pleasure, and he may delegate duties to them as he sees fit. The *Ragnvaldr* is made up to ten in number by the Forseti, three dwarves who settle legal disputes. The Forseti are said to be the purest of dwarves, and sometimes referred to as the 'Snow-white', which also describes the colour of their beards.

8 I myself served as served as a bodyguard to Sundin when he was a *Stridenvaldr*. This was deeply unorthodox and earned him a lot of notoriety. When asked why he had appointed a human to be his bodyguard he answered, 'They're taller than us, you jack-ass; they can see trouble coming long before we do.' Sundin was ever outspoken and this, along with his not being a noble, led to his subsequent demotion.

to do anything else and are essentially thugs in the service of nobles' sons, rather than actual soldiers.

FÖRBINÐA

Each *trupp* will have a nominated *Förbinda*, who will be the *dvergiir* most skilled in the healing arts. The *Förbinda* is expected to fight and carry out all the duties of his kin, but should any fall his priority changes. The wounded are pulled to the back of the formation, where the *Förbinda* will try to stem any bleeding. Sometimes the *Förbinda*'s duty is to make the last moments of a dwarf comfortable ones.[9]

KULLTRUPP

The *kulltrupp* is a small unit, typically just five dwarves, but sometimes as many as ten depending on the ego of the *Kull* leading it. Two of these *dvergiir* will be adjutants, these dwarves are often waiting the opportunity to become *Stridenvaldr*, but some are veteran *Striden-dirigent*. One *dvergiir* will serve as the *Århundrade* standard bearer. Note: standards are only taken to battles above ground. They serve no use at all in tunnel fighting. Another dwarf in the *kulltrupp* will act as *Förbinda*, just

9 *Förbinda* literally means 'to bind over'. These dwarves are not just responsible for the physical welfare of their *trupp*, but also count it as a point of honour to raise their spirits. They are typically jolly fellows, expansive, hard-drinking and always ready with a filthy joke. Much of dwarf humour seems preoccupied with the endowments of elves (small), the size of human beards (also small) and the intelligence of goblins (limited). It is fair to say the dwarves are entirely preoccupied by size.

as in a regular *trupp*. Nervous officers often have two *Förbinda* in their *trupp*, which is a waste of their talents, but such are the traditions of our glorious leaders.

BATTLEFIELD PROMOTION

A *Stridenvaldr* can assume command of the *Århundrade* if the *Kull* is lost in battle. The *Kull* will make provision for death and appoint one of his officers, the most able leader among the *Stridenvaldr*, as '*Första*'. The *Första* will have been entrusted with the battle plan (although if the *Kull* is dead it can be assumed that the plan, such as it was, has been abandoned). It's a quirk of dwarf society that *Stridenvaldr* don't seem to be very competent at fighting. They are very good at standing around and telling other *dvergiir* what to do, which is exactly what we need more of.[10]

STORVALDR

A *Storvaldr* only takes to the field of battle (or the tunnels of war; let us remember that much of our fighting is done below ground) in the gravest of circumstances.[11] A *Storvaldr* has his own *trupp*, comprising of an honour

10 I have always assumed dwarves had escaped the clutches of sarcasm. For a dwarf to speak in a less than forthright manner is unheard of. Reading this sentence aloud, I can't help but wonder if Sundin had spent too much time among humans. Or specifically, with me.

11 *Storvaldr* is the *dvergiir* word for king. Its most direct translation is 'High Ruler'. It is a grave time indeed if a king takes to the field of battle; dwarf nobility prefers to direct wars from the comfort of their halls.

guard of his oldest veterans and friends. Usually the *stor-trupp* is only ten strong, and the *Storvaldr* will commandeer ten more dwarves from among the *Århundrade*. This is not ideal, and takes the most skilled soldiers from their *trupp* when their *dirigent* needs them most. Should a commandeered dwarf survive the engagement, he will return to his *trupp* with much honour. In time he may be called on again, and may even become a regular member of the *stor-trupp*.

Few things cause dwarves to flee, but the fall of their *Storvaldr* will likely be one of them. It goes without saying the *Storvaldr* must be protected at all times. However, he is of little use if he appears to be hiding at the back of the field with the mangonels.

VANÒACRUPP

Vandatrupp are not attached to an *Århundrade* and rarely fight; they do not possess a military rank, but are given the same level of respect. *Vandatrupp* are small squads of dwarves, typically three to five, that carry messages between our citadels. They are expert trackers, climbers and hikers, drawing on physical reserves that are impressive even by dwarven standards. Some even ride ponies.[12] Like all dwarves, they are trained to fight, but should not be expected to do so. In some cases *vandatrupp* operating

12 Dwarves are deeply uncomfortable when mounted. Their feet rarely reach the stirrups and their temperament has a poor effect on their steeds. Placing a dwarf on a mule is not really a solution for their problems with horses – mules are possibly the only creatures in existence as stubborn as the dwarves themselves.

in unison have held mountain passes from enemies who had the advantage of numbers. These dwarves are led by a *Vanda-dirigent.*

SKULÐA

Skulda are work-shy drunkards that are not to be trusted around womenfolk. During peace time they are worth precisely as much as a bucket of piss. They are, however, a regular feature of dwarven society, resting a notch or two above that of *Sperasska.*[13] Like the *vandertrupp*, *skulda* are not formally part of the dwarven military, and are not part of the *Århundrade.* Indeed, most of the time they are not even welcome in the citadel. The *skulda* are storytellers and recorders of epics. Tales of the *skulda* form the backbone of dwarven history, and while I would not trust a *skulda* further than I could throw him, I would never doubt the veracity of an epic. Although troublesome, *skulda* do have a positive effect on soldiers, who fight harder and aspire to greater things when in the presence of these rakish storytellers. It is my utmost recommendation that you kick these tricksters out of the citadel the moment hostilities end. If you want anything resembling a quiet life you will follow this advice to the letter. The locks on the doors to your daughter's chamber should be checked and rechecked.

13 *Sperasska* are outcast dwarves. The word literally means 'kicked out'. Some dwarves choose to become outcast, but many are convicted criminals or oathbreakers. The *skulda* by contrast are not outcast, just a bloody nuisance. They compose great epics in verse about moments in dwarf history, and it is for this reason that a *Kull* will be unwilling to go to war without one or two of these disreputable types in attendance.

MERCENARIES

No subject divides dwarves as much as the use of human mercenaries. Many have never forgiven the humans for luring the dwarves of Voss Traish away from the Union of Dwarven Peoples. Others differ, claiming the dwarves of Voss Traish were ever an aloof lot, preferring the lanky, beardless ones to their own kin.

Most humans are less useful than a one-legged goblin at an arse-kicking contest, especially when it comes to fighting below ground. Dwarf citadels are made for dwarves, so it goes without saying that humans over five feet tall are going to a have a rough time. When below ground, human mercenaries spend more time suffering from self-inflicted concussions than fighting.

Above ground is a different matter. Humans are competent horsemen and able scouts. They can move many times faster than dwarves, relaying messages to other *trupp* or even distant citadels. While their discipline is often poor and their morale laughable, they can be persuaded to hold their ground for the right price. Human mercenary companies should be considered when grave casualties are expected. However, they are canny, and will not tolerate being needlessly sacrificed. Note also that it takes a long time for most human mercenary companies to march from the Kingdom of Arendsonn to our citadels, particularly Voss Jur and Voss Colg.[14]

ħulꝺuRfolka

The *huldurfolka* were the first creations of our old masters. They are as wise as they are tall, and as terrible in battle as they are old. Seven times the height of a dwarf, they are beings of living rock with bright gemstones for eyes. Many *huldurfolka* live in relative peace in the mountains, but a handful live among the dwarves. Each citadel has a guardian who has been joined with

14 Which would explain why the dwarves from Voss Colg are so damnably unfriendly and often outright xenophobic. In general, the dwarves distrust of anyone not dwarf can be overcome by the prospect of turning a profit through trade, or three flagons of ale. Not so the dwarves of Voss Colg. Rumours of my gambling debts at this citadel have been greatly exaggerated.

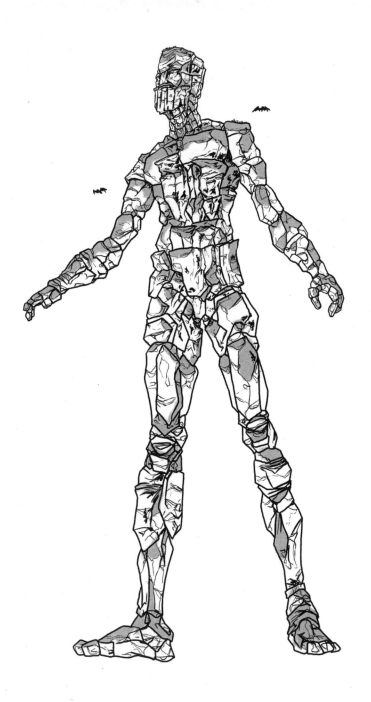

them from the time of the rebellion.[15] While these giant elementals are intimidating in the extreme, they are reluctant to venture abroad, rarely leaving the citadels they have sworn oaths to protect. As such, they are purely a defensive ally, but a welcome one all the same.

Those *huldurfolka* that live in the mountains are reluctant to become embroiled in the affairs of the younger races, and studiously stay apart. They can, however, be depended upon for old lore and advice, even if they can be somewhat cryptic.[16]

15 Only Voss Kilda has more than one of the *huldurfolka* sleeping beneath its halls. One of those sleeping beneath it, Vathhrudniir, is the oldest of all the *huldurfolka*. Dwarves believe he will only awaken for a great battle known to all dwarves as the Day of Reckoning.

16 One of the great dwarven tales recounts how Lokiir Eld-Kron, a famous *skulda* and trickster, stole ten leather rings from the *huldurfolka* Menja. These rings were subsequently sold to the dwarf kings. We know them today as the Auroch Belts of Strength. Five of the belts are still at large, and command a high price on the open market. You can read more about these in Chapter 6: Dwarven Equipment.

3

TACTICS OF THE DWARVES

*'And do you know what the three "T"s of dwarf
tactics are? Tenacity, tenacity, TENACITY!'*

Striden-dirigent Sundin Hallestøm drilling novices
on the finer points of dwarf warfare.

BELOW GROUND

A great deal of dwarf fighting is done below ground,
in defence of the citadels. The elves make a fortress
of the forest, the humans erect shoddy walls,[1] but who
can deny the durability of a mountain? A citadel is about
more than just defence; it is an ancestral home with a

---

1 Dwarf criticism of human architectural methods, particularly those of the
Arends, is a source of much pleasure, not unlike sport. While dwarves would
find it difficult to entrust a human with fairly basic tasks, they would rather
fall on their axes than ask a human for help during the construction of
buildings. I was once memorably told to 'put that chisel down, before you
hurt yourself, or my sensibilities' by a master stoneworker.

long history and many strong associations. The tireless work of countless families has supported the construction of every hall, home and corridor. Each proud gallery and silent vault, every bridge and lofty balcony – all have been hewn from the rock by the patient labours of *dvergiir*. This is why we fight so hard, and this is why we will never surrender. I set down my thoughts on fighting below ground in Chapter 8 of this book.

ABOVE GROUND

Let there be no confusion: taking to the field of battle is a grim undertaking. We lack the mobility of other races, and while we are sturdy and stout, we lack the ability to redeploy soldiers as the course of the battle dictates. Dwarves, by and large, deal with the problem in front of them, and worry about what comes next in due course.[2] We have no truck with horses, do not stoop to *ginning* and enchantment, and lack the fleet-footed and far-ranging scouts of the humans and elves. We take our fate as we find it and make the enemy pay a price in blood for every yard they advance. Our implacable morale, unbreakable breastplates and solid shields let us endure the worst the enemy can set against us.

2 If this sounds distinctly short-sighted then you'd be absolutely right. Dwarves paint themselves into corners both literally and figuratively. I advise caution should you ever try to explain to a dwarf he might not be thinking far enough ahead.

NO SURRENDER

Dwarves do not surrender. The battles of hundreds of years have girded our hearts. The deteriorating relationship with the elves and the calamitous siege of Korlahsia leave us expecting nothing but death from the elder race. Likewise the orcs, who, until the last fifty years, when they have fallen into the habit of returning our nobles to us for a ransom, were ever a murderous lot.[3] Goblins are a far more flighty foe, but what they lack in resolve they make up for in numbers. There is one thing common to all of these creatures: they can all run faster than a dwarf.

Retreating from a foe who has a matching pace is a risky ordeal. The moment you turn your back on an enemy you should consider yourself dead. Only fate itself can save you in this circumstance – perhaps your opponent will become distracted by another attacker, might lose his footing, might decide to fall back.[4] But if an enemy can outpace you, death is almost inevitable, and only a fool would expose his back to it. It is for this reason we dwarves give ground slowly and under the cover of shields and armour.

Listen carefully for the sound of the *visundr* horn; a single blast will signal that an advance is no longer tenable. Should you find yourself the penultimate survivor of your

3 This ransoming of nobles was started by Kani Breakspeare, *Ur-Khagan* of several orc tribes. He is the author of the sister companion to this tome, *The Orc Harrowing*. Dwarves ransomed in this way are usually returned minus their beards, but no one likes to mention this.

4 Not as uncommon as you may think. Self-preservation becomes a tantalising prospect when a fighter is presented with the option of pushing on into the enemy line, even if the closest enemy warrior is fleeing.

unit then you should fight back to back with your kin, make your peace with your ancestors, and take a grim harvest of any enemy who ventures within range.[5]

The CORNERSTONE

The Cornerstone formation has rightly earned its name, for it forms the basis of all dwarf warfare, proving time and again to be as impervious as its namesake. It is the foundation on which we lay our battle plans. Dwarf armies are slow to advance, and it is not practical to expect our enemies always to hurl themselves at us with frenzied abandon. Although many do, especially the goblins, who only rarely bring even a few dozen javelins. Recently, orc tribes have adopted ranged weapons to soften up their enemies. Orc bows are crudely constructed and prone to mishap. The arrows they fletch are little better. However, orc archers can prove to be distracting and even lethal to those caught off-guard. Where elves fire in volleys, orcs fire at will. Coordinating the holding up of shields against the elves' concentrated arrow fire is easier than trying to second guess the random shooting of the orcs.

Humans and elves are predisposed to ranged combat because they lack the stomach for close-quarters fighting, and it is against these enemies that the Cornerstone formation is most effective.

5 Dwarf folk tales abound of 'the last two survivors' of any given *Århundrade*. Invariably, these two dwarves go on to train the next generation, then die heroically years later in a hard-fought battle. The names of the dwarves, the citadels and the battles themselves change, but the basic format of the story stays the same.

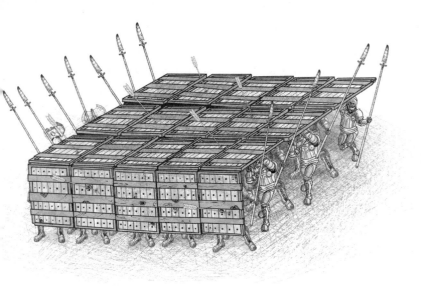

The formation sees a *trupp* form into ranks. Each *Striden-dirigent* will have his own preference for formation. I favour a *trupp* of twenty dwarves arranged in four ranks of five. Those dwarves in the first rank hold their shields in front of them, while the dwarves in the following three ranks lock their shields together to form a roof over the unit.

Arrows that are fired indirectly, as many are during large conflicts, descend at an angle. These arrows rarely puncture the stout shields of the dwarves, and will skitter off. Arrows fired directly at the front rank will cause more problems, but the shield wall will hold firm.[6] Maintaining this formation is essential for closing ground with enemies that employ and rely on a high number of missile troops. You should adopt this formation even

6 You can read more about the dwarf shield, or *skydd*, in Chapter 5: Dwarven Armour.

when facing the orcs, who have grown steadily more cunning over the last century. The Cornerstone is an intimidating sight, even for the most jaded of veterans, and should not be underestimated by our leaders.

TÖRNE ANÐ ÞUGGTANÐ

It is the crossbow, ranked behind lines of spears, that deters heavy cavalry. The bolts fired can punch through plate armour and shields. Even those projectiles that do not cause injury are distracting in the extreme. These weapons can punish lightly armoured units and cause a collapse in morale that saves on the business of fighting at close quarters. An orc *Khagan* and his retinue frequently adopt heavy armour, making them perfect targets for crossbows. The weight of the armour slows the orcs, allowing the dwarves a few extra seconds to reload and shoot. However, do not depend on orcs to simply lie down and die after the first shot. Their tolerance for pain is legendary; their ability to endure grievous wounds should not be understated. Using crossbows against a troll is pointless; these brutes only fall to the massive trauma of hammers and axes.[7] They are not unlike trees in some regards, and should be treated similarly.

7 Trolls are a constant worry to dwarves, and particularly in the depths of winter. The trolls have difficulty sating their huge appetites and view the halls in much the same way a dwarf views a full pantry. The worst of these attacks feature three trolls attacking together. The dwarves call these gatherings a troika. Even the bravest of dwarf veterans look uncertain at times like these. This has led to a strange hand gesture among the dwarves, who hold up three fingers at those who have insulted them. I took this gesture to mean 'may a troika be upon your house', which is a fierce curse, even from a dwarf.

тhe Veiled hαMMer

A tactic I favour is to deploy crossbows on each flank to deter the enemy. You should place two *trupp* with shields at your centre. These two *trupp* form a Cornerstone around dwarves bearing two-handed axes or hammers. The shield formation of the Cornerstone protects those dwarves who would not normally enjoy its benefit. Once you have closed ground with the enemy, under supporting fire from the crossbows, you may relax the Cornerstone formation and enter close quarters. The appearance of *dvergiir* bearing two-handed weapons will be an unwelcome one, and these warriors will be able to hunt down heavier-armoured troops that others would find difficult to defeat.

This is a perfect example of dwarves working together for a common purpose, to overcome shared obstacles. Should unexpected difficulty be encountered you can re-inforce the line with any units you may have in reserve.[8]

Some enemies, and veteran enemy commanders, are well acquainted with the Veiled Hammer. It may be necessary to form an additional *trupp* into a Cornerstone as a distraction, flanking the *trupp* protecting the dwarves without shields. This will keep the enemy guessing and he'll be reluctant to redeploy any forces until you have dropped the ruse and relaxed the formation.

8 While undeniably war-like, dwarves are not above a modicum of caution. Holding units in reserve is not as unlikely as it may seem. The idea of veteran dwarves, half-crazed by war and whisky, chewing on their shields in anticipation, is useful propaganda spread by the *skulda*. In reality dwarves are more circumspect.

This tactic is dependent on your forces having access to onager.[9] You will want at least five. Deploy the onager on one flank, but hidden from enemy eyes. You can do this by using shallow trenches, large tents, or by clustering dwarves around them. The timing of this tactic should be meticulous, and the expertise of your onager crews will need to be without question.

In essence, you will punish one flank of the enemy forces with the onager, as well as crossbows where possible. When the enemy is sufficiently weakened you can then engage using *dvergiir* armed with two-handed weapons. This application of raw force will cause the enemy units to flee or be destroyed entirely. From there you can attack down the enemy line from his own flank. Make sure your primary units do not advance too far ahead. If they do they may find themselves struck by projectiles from the onager, or without adequate support from those *trupp* forming the main battle line. While losses are to be expected, you are not sacrificing the unit.

Tip OF The Spear

This tactic abandons the principle of reserves and commits the force in two parts. You will draw up a battle line much as you would at any other engagement. The forces you would otherwise have kept in reserve form a column.

9 Onager, the stone-throwing catapults of the dwarves, are covered in more detail in Chapter 6 of this tome. The dwarves are mightily proud of these engineering marvels.

The head of the column forms part of the battle line. This is the titular tip of the spear. When the enemy comes within range the column will advance ahead of the main line, the tip pushing through the enemy line. You will need around five *trupp* to make this tactic worthwhile, not including those forces that form the line. Naturally, the spear will consist of warriors equipped for close-quarters fighting. All crossbows should be deployed to the flanks to deter the enemy from circling your forces and disrupting the plan.[10]

Once the spear has made sufficient headway you can give the order to break out. The enemy, whose line is now divided in two, will struggle to rally against the great numbers of dwarves attacking their flanks. The enemy line loses cohesion at this point, and you must be on your guard for freak occurrences. Sudden reversals occur all too often when a leader thinks victory is assured.

10 This happens more than the dwarves like to admit, and many engage-ments descend into chaos where the dwarves fight back to back, a stout and unyielding island of warriors surrounded on all sides by the enemy. Al-though none would confess it publicly, I believe the dwarves like it this way. 'We can kill more of them, more quickly, and not have to worry about being stabbed in the back,' muttered one dwarf, deep in his cups one night.

4

WEAPONS OF OUR FATHERS

*'You wouldn't try to smash a square peg into
a round hole, so why try to kill a troll
with a knitting needle?'*

Striden-dirigent Sundin Hallestøm explaining why swords
are a poor choice of weapon in the mountains.

KNIFE

No dwarf worth his beard goes anywhere without a
knife. They are not simply stabbing weapons, but
tools with everyday uses. Miners, tanners, carpenters, and
artisans of every persuasion all carry knives. There is
no prohibition on carrying these weapons in society,
although dwarves carrying more than two are likely to
be looked upon as troublemakers or *sperasska*. It is often
the case that dwarves, particularly young ones, become
lost due to the labyrinthine nature of our architecture.
Add to this the goblin tendency to make camps in the

unused corners of our citadels and the results can be tragic. This is why no dwarf can afford to be unarmed, even within the supposedly safe confines of our halls.[1]

Dwarf knives are usually five to nine inches long and feature a broad, flat blade. A smooth edge runs down one side with a serrated edge opposite. This serrated side is for sawing through rope. *Förbinda* use that edge to cut injured dwarves out of leather armour in order to treat their wounds.[2]

The knife also bears a sturdy crosspiece, from which extends a single hoop. The knife can be pressed into service as a spear by slotting a length of wood, such as a quarterstaff, into the hoop and fastening it with twine. This is a favoured tactic of the *vandatrupp*, who hunt wild boars through this means without the burden of carrying spears.

NÄVEN

No weapon quite encapsulates the dwarven spirit like the hammer. Once a simple tool, it became a symbol of defiance against the Great Drakes and continues to serve us as a trusted weapon till this very day. There are

---

1 The words 'halls' and 'citadels' are used almost interchangeably by dwarves. A citadel is essentially a grouping of dwarf halls, connected by corridors. Often these halls are in close proximity to the mines that have been claimed by the industrious families that work them. Each hall is home to a *Kull*, his retinue and the families that are related to that *Kull* by blood or marriage. They are crowded and bustling affairs, often hosting scenes of great drama and a lot of shouting. Words like 'privacy' and 'solitude' rarely enter into the *dvergiir* lexicon.

2 Tales abound of battlefield amputations, but I find this unlikely.

very few adequate defences to a hammer strike. Blades struggle to parry them, shields shatter and split. Even those wearing the heaviest of armours suffer when struck. Hammers inflict severe concussions, snap ribs, and break knees with impunity.[3] Nobles of all races wear plate armour, even the elves who often favour speed over protection. Enemies who survive a beating from a hammer don't always survive being prised out of their mangled armour. Lighter troops such as goblins and elf skirmishers often fall after just two well-placed blows. Leather armour provides little protection from broken bones.

For many years the hammer had a wooden shaft, but these days it is more often made from metal for durability. Wood invariably shatters or breaks; a steel shaft wrapped with a leather grip is much more reliable. Contrary to what other races say, we have never called this weapon a 'war hammer'. It takes only a cursory glance for even the most foolish dwarf to tell whether a hammer is fit for war or for nailing shingles to a roof.[4]

At close quarters, only enemies bearing spears pose a

3 Knee injuries are far and away the most prevalent of wounds when facing the *dvergiir*. Dwarves rarely speak of this, and are much more taken with describing how opponents were decapitated (almost exclusively goblins), or how they 'smote ruin upon' the enemy. Generally, dwarves kneecap those who attack them and bash their brains out as they lie prone. It is not a glamorous way to fight, but then few ways are.

4 That said, a dwarf will use absolutely anything if it means he has a chance of killing a goblin. Tales of dwarves who 'rent their foes apart with their bare hands' are not always the exaggerations one might expect. Dwarves have an impossibly strong grip. With this in mind, it's worth being wary of the dwarf handshake, which is the least friendly greeting in all of Nedanförvärld.

significant threat to dwarves armed with hammers. The elves often use a glaive-type weapon, so it's best to use crossbows to kill units armed in this way.[5] Those dwarves armed with a hammer must also bear a shield if they hope to close with the enemy rather than fall to his arrows. Shields, much like the mail and plate we wear, are at the core of the dwarven philosophy of war.

ᴄᴡᴏ-ʜᴀɴᴆᴇᴆ ʜᴀᴍᴍᴇʀ

Fighting below ground is a cramped and brutal affair. Light is poor, footing is uncertain, and it feels as if the rock itself is pressing in.[6] At times like these a shield is not always practical. Enclosed fighting doesn't allow for the shield wall tactics a *trupp* would use on the open field of battle. Combat in tunnels makes attack the best form of defence. And for this, what better weapon than a two-handed hammer? This weapon is often called a 'Goblin-smiter' by veteran *dvergiir*, and with good cause. One well-placed blow has spelt the end of many of our most hated enemies. Dwarves of short beards would do well to remember that the two-handed hammer does have limitations. These weapons are little better than tomb markers when facing elves with swords. The speed and

5 Sundin is, of course, referring to 'Indignation', the great spear of the elves. You can read more about this and other features of elven fighting in *The Aelfir Art of War,* available from the University of Hoim, or the Kindling Bookstore.

6 A dwarf elder, named Klaus Trow, has spent much time studying the effects of cramped environments on the human psyche. He names this anxious state as a 'Föbia'. Thus, it has become known as Klaus Trow's Föbia.

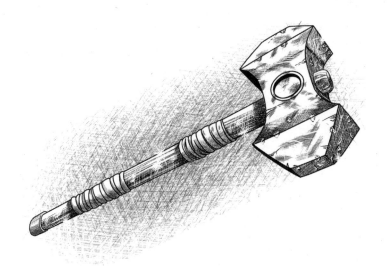

accuracy of elven swordsmen is hard to match, and a *dvergiir* is at a distinct disadvantage due to the hammer's cumbersome swing. The weapon is some use against orcs, especially those orcs in the *Khagan*'s retinue, who wear plate armour, and the hated trolls.

The two-handed hammer usually features a steel head mounted on a shaft of seasoned oak. The shaft is wrapped and bound with leather or canvas, which improves grip. A small hole is drilled roughly six inches from the end. Many dwarves thread a cord of leather through the hole and tie it off around their wrist. If they should be unlucky enough to lose grip on the hammer, it will not fall to the ground. This simple precaution has saved the lives of many dwarves down through the centuries.

The hammer is double-headed, meaning that a dwarf is just as dangerous on the backswing as he is on the initial attack. Oftentimes the backswing is an unpleasant and fatal surprise for those unseasoned opponents. The downside, of course, is that the two-handed hammer is taxing, even to the endurance of dwarves. These fighters need to be pulled back every so often in order to compose themselves and regain their strength.

TALONGEN

Axes are seen as the archetypal weapon of the *dvergiir*, but in truth, the secret of their construction was learned from the elves. It is for this reason many dwarves shun the axe, which seems foolhardy. I enjoy harbouring a grudge as much as the next dwarf, but even I can see the merits of this weapon.[7] Like the hammer, it began life as a tool, but one that quickly found itself pressed into service when danger reared its head.

Axes, like most hammers, are best used one-handed with a shield carried in the off-hand.[8] Where the axe is superior to the hammer is in the ability to split armour. When the short and wedge-like blade of an axe is coupled with the strength of a dwarf the results are impressive. Even well-crafted armour yields easily to the axes of the dwarves. It is perhaps for this reason that axes are favoured by veteran *dvergiir*, who know they are likely to

7 I refrained from telling Sundin how the *Ur-Khagan* Kani Breakspeare had a huge collection of axes, mostly of dwarven manufacture. I think this might have soured his appreciation for the weapon. You can read more about the orcs in *The Orc Harrowing*, available from the University of Hoim, or the Kindling Bookstore.

8 An exception to this would be *Keivan 'Biletongue' Russ*: famous on account of his strongly worded opinions and great skill with an axe in each hand. Keivan was an especially tall sperasska from Voss Colg.

be called on to face heavily armoured opponents. One should not seek to penetrate where the armour is strongest, but instead strike at the hinges and joints. No warrior ever carried the day by making his task harder for himself.

Dwarf weaponsmiths forge this weapon with a sharp, straight pick on the reverse of the axe head. This part of the axe is especially good for punching through breastplates and causing chest wounds. Once an opponent suffers a wounded lung he is effectively a dead elf walking.[9] The pick is also invaluable for traversing mountainsides and is useful for climbing. Lightweight versions of this weapon exist, often touted as ice axes by their sellers.

TWO-HANDED AXE

The two-handed axe fighting style is deeply revered among dwarves, especially as it has had many notable adherents through the centuries. It is a weapon that demands much vigour and is unforgiving to those who make mistakes. A dwarf's timing must be impeccable. Those who overstep or find themselves off balance are likely to find themselves dead a heartbeat later. Naturally a shield is not an option (although some dwarves do attach a smaller shield, the buckler, to their wrists). What the wielder loses in defence he makes up for greatly with the sheer amount of damage he can inflict.

---

9 Elves feature quite a lot in the dwarves' turns of phrase. A 'dead elf walking' is anyone suffering a fatal wound. 'It's all elf to me' means something is unfathomable, whereas to 'smell an elf' is to believe some act of betrayal or deception is afoot. To 'let sleeping elves lie' is to leave a matter undisturbed that would cause issue if mentioned.

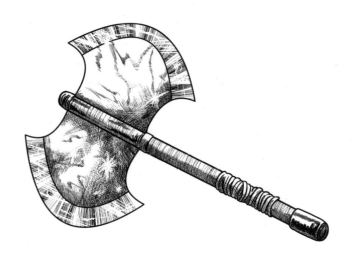

Axes, as mentioned above, excel at breaking through armour and splitting shields. They are pure overkill when used against goblins. One moment's lapse of attention can spell a dwarf's end on the barb of a lucky spear thrust by the crudest of these low creatures. However, the two-handed axe should never be discounted when facing orcs, elves or humans, particularly those orcs who have troll blood in their veins. These towering opponents are Hel walking for any dwarf.[10] The two-handed axe is perhaps the only weapon worth using against trolls.

10 The dwarfs speak often of Hel, a being they say rules the underworld. This was not always the case. Hel is a recent coinage that occurred around the same time the elves suffered their mysterious catastrophe in Umber Reach. When I pressed the dwarves about Hel they simply declared she was a 'dark star sent to bring misery to the lives of all'. I am convinced there is some correlation between Hel and Khaeris, and possibly between Hel and the Umber Wraiths too. Describing something as 'Hel walking' or 'Hel on legs' means the opponent is fearsome indeed.

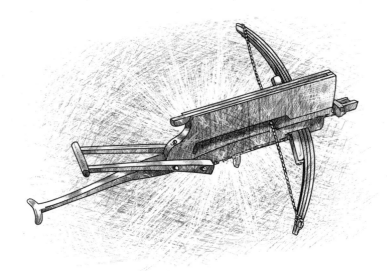

ḣUGGꞬCANꝊ

The crossbow is what sets the dwarves apart from the other races. The elves have their longbows, the orcs have their mauls, but the weapon that is uniquely dwarven is the crossbow. The human version of this weapon is but a pale imitation, prone to malfunctioning often, and with disastrous consequences. Our mastery of tension, torsion, and the intricate mechanisms of the crank system allow us to build crossbows that reload faster and strike more accurately.[11] Some dwarves prefer the windlass system of drawing back the string, while others swear by a crank device that uses a rack and pinion. Maintenance

11 Dwarves armed with crossbows often complain they are missing out on the action while reloading. This has given rise to the expression 'getting a bit cranky'. Alternately, a 'crank' is a dwarf who spends a lot of time aggravating his kin, or winding them up.

of crossbows is a serious matter: the wood should be oiled with care and the mechanism thoroughly cleaned and oiled. The bow, or lath, is often made from a composite of yew, bone and sinew, bound together with animal tendon. These days we build the crossbow with a steel lath and a linen string, which gives our crossbows an effective range of 200 feet.

Dwarves using crossbows are required to venture above ground one day a week and participate in target practice. It is all the better if they return with something edible into the bargain.[12] Sometimes a *trupp* on target practice stumbles across a threat to the citadel and are the first dwarves to raise the alarm; yet another reason to continue this tradition.

TÖRNE

A spear is not an obvious choice of weapon for a dwarf but their uses below and above ground cannot be understated. A reasonable first impression is that a spear would be unwieldy in the tight and winding tunnels that run beneath our citadels. However, a spear gives a dwarf an unprecedented amount of reach. Goblins need to work hard to manoeuvre past the point to attack the defending dwarf. Three dwarves armed with spears can make a bloodbath of a corridor. However, what goblins lack in weapons and armour they make up for in numbers, so

12 Hunting is the leading way of keeping dwarf crossbowmen well practised. No one wants to be the dwarf that returns home without any food for his kin. That said, what the dwarves possess in accuracy they sadly lack in trapping skills. Stealth is not a word that features often in the dwarf lexicon.

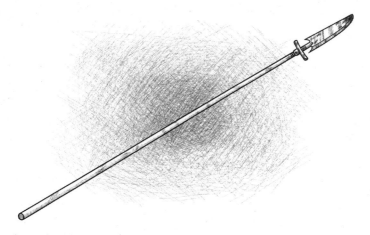

these battles are not just ones of skill, but of endurance too.

While crossbows deter heavy cavalry, spears are essential for turning it aside. A *trupp* armed with spears is a prickly proposition for any attackers. When spears are combined with armour and shields, a *trupp* can withstand charges from light infantry. Momentum is usually the advantage of our attackers; very rarely do dwarves get the opportunity to charge our enemies. However, a dwarf with a spear is an almost intractable opponent, braced to receive the enemy with spear tips waiting to impale the unwary. The dwarf can release the spear in order to use an axe or hammer should the charger survive to get into close-quarters combat.

On an extended campaign the spear also has the advantage of being the same length as a tent pole. You may not think this massively useful until you need to set up additional tents as field hospitals. Many are the times an orc raid has made off with the better part of the supply train. For some reason there always seems to be a shortage of tent poles.

SVÄRD

The svärd is often a weapon sought after by the nobility, especially *Stor-striden*.[13] But it is neither use nor ornament to any respectable dwarf. It is not, and should not ever be, part of a dwarf's standard kit.[14] Dwarves are not agile; we are not quick. We do not have long arms and the majority of our kin are ill-suited to the nuances of swordplay. A dwarf's advantage lies in his great strength, a strength that is better served with an axe or hammer.

The convention for naming a svärd originated with the elves, and should remain with that sickly and foppish race of tree-fondlers. It is a sad reminder of how impressionable humans are that they follow this ridiculous fashion. Therefore when dwarves approach and boast they wear 'Goblinbane' or 'Raven's Friend' on their hip I give them short shrift.[15] I'd much rather a dwarf spend his money on several spears than on one svärd of supposedly fine quality.

Elves imbue their weapons with *ginning*, but dwarf weapons are better by virtue of being made purely with

13 *Svärd* is the *dvergiir* word for sword. The Arends undoubtedly adopted the word, which explains why they call them 'svords'. I assumed this was just part of their ridiculous accent but it seems I was wrong.

14 Standard kit for a dwarf consists of a weapon, a shield (if it is appropriate), a backup weapon, a knife, a bedroll, a canteen of water, a canteen of ale, a leather coat, a full suit of mail and a helmet. Additional canteens of ale are popular, as are satchels containing whole roast chickens. Only a dwarf could easily carry that much equipment. I don't advise any human to try to compete.

15 Could a dwarf give any other sort of shrift?

craftsmanship. Make no mistake, dwarf weapons are disposable: they become blunt, the metal tires, the hafts snap or become brittle. No creature who ever lived longer than a human expects otherwise. The best you can hope for is that the metal in the original weapon can be reforged. If it were up to me all dwarves with svärds would be forced to reforge them into something more useful, even if it were only a ploughshare.

THROWING AXES

These weapons are best left in the hands of specialists and have few uses on the field of battle. They are most often used by dwarves in *vandertrupp* or those acting as bodyguards to *Stridenvaldr*. The throwing axe is lighter than the standard axe, and some dwarves wear a brace of three such weapons. They are, to my mind, a last resort, and have no use in *trupp*-based warfare. Dwarves of little beard have sought to use a throwing axe against an opponent who is already engaged in combat, only to strike the very dwarf they were attempting to assist. Such actions are only figments of tall tales and ale-fuelled fancies. These weapons are also beloved by *skulda* and criminals, which also sours my opinion of them.

QUARTERSTAFF

The quarterstaff is not a weapon used in the regular armies of dwarves, but is a handy ally to *vandatrupp*. It aids walking by taking some of the strain away from the legs, and even provides support over difficult ground. In combat, the staff is good for keeping goblins at bay – the reach of the weapon is adequate defence. The aim of the staff is to render opponents unconscious by application of a heavy strike just below the ear or at the base of the skull. They can then be tied up and questioned at leisure, which is how *vandatrupp* uncover information from the goblins. Orcs rarely reveal anything of use, even with the most horrific application of interrogation.

5

ÐWARVEN ARMOUR

'There're only two good reasons any dwarf sleeps without some armour on. The first is to pleasure his woman, the second is to invite Hel. I know which I prefer.'

Striden-dirigent Sundin Hallestøm drilling
novices on fieldcraft.

STRIÐENROCK

A padded leather coat is the absolute minimum a dwarf with any sort of beard will appear in.[1] The coat is typically made from auroch skin treated by tanners. Some citadels are very particular about where they get the leather from, while others are happy to trade

---

1 Having 'any sort of beard, even a short one' is a matter of great pride. Orcs have adopted the practice of cutting a dwarf's beard off and ransoming him back to his people. Such dwarves are obsessed with regaining their lost honour. The orcs on the other hand welcome the chance to fight the dwarf again. I mention more about this in *The Orc Harrowing: An Oral History.*

for it, often with the Arends, who are better at needle-work than they are at fighting. *Stridenrock* is often used as a term to describe not just the coat dwarves wear, but many pieces of leather armour, especially when other armour is worn over the top.

No *stridenrock* would be complete without a hefty belt to cinch it in at the waist. This provides a good place to hang a weapon from. It has been customary for dwarves to wear a belt denoting the colour of their hall or household.[2]

Coats can be short-sleeved, or lack sleeves altogether, although this is unwise in protracted engagements. Some dwarves prefer to have separate padded sleeves that cover the forearm. In doing so they sacrifice a measure of protection at the elbow in exchange for greater mobility. It is often dwarves who fight with two-handed weapons that adopt this mode of armour most eagerly.

OÐNÍÍR-NÄVEN

Odniir-näven are essential for much of our work: smithing and mining to name just two uses.[3] They are also useful in combat; no dwarf wants the backs of their fists laid open with a blade. Blood from wounded hands

2 Tales of dwarves wearing 'belts of silver and gold' are just that, tall tales. Well, perhaps not that tall. The expense of a silver belt would be prohibitive, and as likely as surviving a trip downriver in a leaky barrel.

3 Odniir-näven means 'fist of Odniir', just another reminder of how much esteem the All-Father is afforded, even in having everyday, mundane items named after him. Most dwarves get through a pair of gauntlets a year, and they are common presents at the Mittvinterhelg.

quickly causes loss of grip on the weapon, ultimately spelling out a dwarf's doom. Odniir-näven are crafted from visundr skin, which is softer than the leather from an auroch and therefore more comfortable.[4] These gloves need to be supple in order to wear plate armour gauntlets over the top, although some dwarves find these a hindrance. Lately a visundr-skin glove with mail sewn to the back for additional protection has come into fashion. While not as hard-wearing as a plate gauntlet, the mailed glove does provide a good balance of dexterity and defence.

---

4 Visundr are wild mountain bison. These creatures form the principal diet of the dwarves. Auroch are more of a delicacy and harder to obtain due to being plains-dwelling creatures. Dwarves are not wasteful people, so the bones and tendons are often used in the construction of their famed composite crossbows, while the blood is mixed with minerals and water to make paint.

OXARNACKE

A padded leather collar is strongly recommended for every dwarf no matter how long the beard. This is not just as a measure of protection, but also to provide comfort from mail or plate armour, which will press down on collarbones. The oxarnacke should be worn whenever a dwarf is on duty, as goblin infiltrators are adept at creeping up on lone sentries.[5] These low creatures will try to slash the throats of the unwary, dealing death noiselessly, before intruding further into the citadel. The oxarnacke provides a dwarf with protection from such an ignominious death.[6] I sleep in mine during campaigns, and especially when I'm outside the citadel.

STRIDENKJOL

The upper legs are either protected by the lower portions of the stridenrock, or the dwarf can wear a *kjol* instead.

---

5 All dwarves are called upon to stand guard one night a week as part of their duties to their *Storvaldr*. It a source of endless bitching among the dwarves, although I never quite determined why. Normally the whole issue with a night shift is that you miss out on daylight, but this is not a part of everyday subterranean dwarf life. I settled on the theory that dwarves just enjoy complaining, especially if they feel hard done by for any reason.

6 *Oxarnacke* means 'neck of the auroch' which is to say broad and very strong. Being killed in one's sleep is a fate that offends the dwarf spirit and provokes strong feelings. It is for this reason they set vigorous watches and sleep in as much armour as they can tolerate. In regular speech, a dwarf described as '*oxarnacke*' is one that is thick-skinned and takes little offence, no matter how fierce the goading. These dwarves do exist, and are rare creatures indeed.

The *kjol* is simply a knee-length skirt of padded leather.[7] The problem with this mode of armour is the gap that inevitably shows between each garment, leaving an exposed belly.[8] This typically occurs when one is thrusting forward with a spear, or off balance and unable to defend oneself. While more comfortable for day-to-day wear I would advise against this pairing unless mail or plate is worn over the top of both items.

SPARKA

Dwarf boots almost always reach a dwarf's knees due to our frame. A pair of stout *sparka* should meet the lower edge of the *stridenrock* or *kjol*, providing ample protection. Many dwarves will insist on steel toe cap boots, which I would recommend if you have the funds.[9] The best *sparka* are crafted from auroch leather, but visundr

7 Dwarf womenfolk wear a *kjol* every day, often with a sleeveless leather coat. The male dwarf has no problem in adopting the *kjol* for wartime. In addition to wearing *kjol*, female dwarves grow their hair as long as they can, arranging it in great plaits, which further helps discern one gender from the other.

8 It is impractical for most races to strike for a dwarf's belly. However, the goblins are particularly focused on this area. Factor in the goblin's penchant for poisoned or diseased blades and the prospect of being wounded anywhere becomes a grim one. Such wounds need treating immediately, lest the infection take hold; hence the proliferation of *Förbinda*.

9 Dwarves will hurt an enemy in just about any way they can manage. They are not above kicking an opponent, especially over the sides of the chasms that occur underground. When they kick an enemy into an abyss they often shout, 'This is *sparka*', and then laugh to themselves for many minutes. I never found out why.

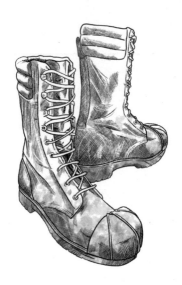

leather is almost as good and it has a warming lining that is good for outdoors. It is for this reason visundr *sparka* are popular with the *vandatrupp* messengers.

KLÄNKE

The secrets of dwarf mail construction are tightly guarded, and for good reason. Ours is the most enduring type of this armour, and the stout links easily turn aside the blades of knives and swords. Stray arrows can also be deflected, but one should not hope to avoid death if caught in the sights of an elf longbow. Crossbows punch through the protection granted by mail, which is why we are so loath to share the secrets of their construction, or let these weapons fall into the hands of our enemies. Even human crossbows should give a mail-armoured dwarf pause for concern.

Klänke adds a greater layer of safety to the leather

stridenrock that forms the basis of all dwarf armour. *Klänke* is not cheap, and takes many days of careful and meticulous construction. Although heavy, it does little to impede the natural strength of the dwarves, and the trade-off between agility and protection is a favourable one.

KLÄNKEKRONA

Klänkekrona, while uncomfortable, should always be worn if you can afford it and certainly if you have lost your helmet.[10] It is simply a close-fitting hood of mail

---

10 *Klänkekrona* is 'crown of links', or a coif. I did ask why the dwarves prefix the word '*länk*' (link) with the letter 'k'. Sundin shrugged his shoulders and replied, 'Have you ever heard a dwarf trying to sneak about in mail armour?'

links. A leather skullcap is provided for the weight of the metal to rest on, preventing the links from cutting into the forehead. Dwarves suffer a disproportionate number of head wounds when fighting creatures other than goblins, so it's important to gird yourself as thoroughly as possible. Head wounds bleed like a stuck visundr, causing loss of vision, faintness and shock. It is better to fall back and be treated by the *Förbinda* than to try to keep fighting.

TIMBRE

A simple coat is often worn over mail to keep the links free from the worst excesses of water. Caverns drip and the skies over the mountains rain often. Mail rusts just like any other metal and is Hel to clean. The *timbre* is a cap-sleeve coat that extends as far as the knee. It is always dyed the primary colour of the citadel: red for Century Falls,[11] black for Voss Kilda, deep green for Voss Drun, grey for Voss Colg and dun brown for Voss Jur. Often these coats feature piping at the shoulder in the colour of the household. A broad belt, worn over the top, will also be in the colours of the household. Note that the *timbre* is only worn on duty, guarding the citadel, or in large-scale engagements when it is essential to be able to tell one unit from another at a glance. It is not worn on a day-to-day basis.

11 The dwarves of Century Falls did not always dye their *timbre* red, previously leaving them an unbleached hue. Some dwarves complain that the new colour is further proof of that citadel's excessive wealth, and the influence of the many humans who now live there.

Many dwarves do not carry their weapons from a belt on their hip because it encumbers them in the tunnels.[12] Instead, many dwarves with wear a broad, woven belt over one shoulder, diagonally across their body. This belt will feature a loop that a hand weapon can be slotted into, leaving the hands free for longer journeys or climbing below ground. This belt can also be doubled up and form a sling of sorts for those dwarves sustaining broken or fractured arms.

SKÖLÐÄRM

The most vulnerable parts of a dwarf, after the head, are the forearms. These extremities are often in the line of danger, and it is far easier for an enemy to hack off a limb than a head. Arms should never be left unprotected, as stout and strong as they may be. *Sköldärm* is the general name give to any piece of armour that covers the forearm.[13] It can be made from leather or metal, and the best examples feature a curved rectangular section that extends over the back of the hand, as far as the knuckles. Remember that the *sköldärm* will be worn over the leather coat and mail.

The lighter versions of *sköldärm* are simply additional layers of leather, sometimes lacquered together, stitched

12 It is most certainly not because dwarf weapons are very large, often longer than the legs of the dwarf carrying them. And even if the idea does occur to you that this is so, you would be well advised not to mention it in front of these war-like and quick-tempered people.

13 *Sköld* is another word for shield in the *dvergiir* tongue. *Ärm* simply means arm, so there need be little discussion of the root of that word.

with sinew, and worn over mail. Heavier versions are made from metal, and are just one component of plate armour.

ÐRAKEHJÄRTA

The *drakehjärta* is the heaviest of all armour.[14] It will slow even the sturdiest dwarf when worn in conjunction with layers of leather and mail. Dwarven smiths spend long hours at the anvil beating metal with hammers and using secrets handed down from father to son over many centuries to create it. The breastplate transforms a dwarf from a simple threat to an almost impregnable fighter, easily the match of twenty goblins or a handful of orcs.[15]

Some dwarves think to save themselves some burden by shunning the backplate. This is entirely slovenly and akin to the shirking of human mercenaries. While the majority of threats do come from in front, there is always the chance of being flanked during close-quarters fighting. Certainly in the chaos of tunnel fighting there is opportunity for goblins to find ways around any given bridge or choke point. It is at times like these that they

14 Despite the dwarves long-held enmity with their draconic masters it seems they still hold them in some esteem. *Drakehjärta* literally means 'dragon heart', although I suspect in this instance it is a reference to how enduring and imperishable those mythic creatures are, rather than anything more positive. Surely a drake's heart is a cold and withered thing indeed?

15 This isn't necessarily a simple boast, nor is it evidence of a lack of humility on the dwarves' behalf. Think instead that this is a measure of how much regard dwarves have for *drakehjärta*. Every dwarf would buy his own breastplate if he could, and most likely wear it on feast days and birthdays.

will thrust cruel poniards and dirks through the links of
your mail, into your kidneys.[16] An excruciating wound
to be sure. The same can be said on the battle field,

16 Goblins are possessed of a somewhat manic disregard for their own lives,
often fighting lightly armoured and with a weapon in each hand. I asked
Sundin why the goblins fought in a such a crazed fashion. He simply pointed
to a patch of mushrooms and replied, 'Eat enough of those and you'd start a
fight with the tide and think you could win.'

especially if the line is breached. Once battle is joined, and after the initial fury of the charges, one can never be truly sure who is stood at one's back. It is for this reason a proper suit of *drakehjärta* should include a backplate as well as the breastplate.

hJÄLM

Every dwarf receives a steel helmet on his twentieth birthday. It is a symbol of a life to come, a life that will be spent defending the citadel when the need arises. Dwarf skulls are thick, thicker than elf, goblin and human skulls certainly. Only the orcs and trolls can match us in this area. It is still a poor reason to go to battle unprotected. Our race survived its infancy mining deep tunnels for draconic masters, where rock falls could strike at any time. Concussion, either from stone or enemy, is not a welcome injury. Vital seconds can slip away that should be spent in action. This is why we wear the *hjälm*. Each citadel has its own distinctive *hjälm* and it is by this item you may know where your fellow warriors hail from.

The dwarves of Voss Kilda favour an open-faced *hjälm* sporting horns on each side. The more expensive the *hjälm* the larger the horns. Auroch horns are preferred, but the rank and file soldiers make do with visundr horns. Tales of dwarves goring opponents to death are largely exaggerated.

The dwarves of Voss Jur do not use horns at all, but instead wear a helmet that encloses the top half of the face. There is much to be said for the inclusion of a nose guard, as anyone who has taken even a glancing blow to

the nose will tell you. Being struck in this manner will cause the eyes to water, which in turn makes defending oneself that much harder. A mouth guard is attached as a stylised moustache.

The traditional *hjälm* of Voss Colg also encloses the top half of the face, but has a lower section comprising mail. As mentioned above, head wounds tend to bleed fiercely, and a facial wound is not good for a dwarf's spirit. The mail will protect the dwarf from stray arrows, crossbow bolt ricochets (more common underground) and goblin daggers, which they invariably soil with their own excrement so as to cause infected wounds.[17]

The dwarves of Voss Drun also favour mail in the

17 Note: 'I'm completely shit-faced' in dwarf society does not mean 'to be drunk', as I found out to my own cost. Instead my hosts all assumed I had been stabbed in the face with a goblin's rusty and filth-coated dagger. I had quite a time explaining this particular turn of phrase.

construction of their *hjälm*, but instead have the mail at the back, protecting the neck.[18] The Voss Drun *hjälm* lacks a nose guard, which explains why so many of those noble dwarves have terrible scars and crooked noses.

The dwarves of Voss Traish have adopted a *hjälm* with a prominent nose guard and a horse hair plume. This smacks of distinctly human and elf influences but is an effective means of protecting one's head all the same. The horse hair is dyed red and stiffened with resin so it stands straight in a shocking Mohican. A *Striden-dirigent* may be identified by his plume, which features five bands of black dye, alternating with the red. A *Hojta-dirigent* has four bands of black dye, a

---

18 I kept hearing dwarves referring to their necks but can honestly say that in nine months among them, I never once saw this fabled area. The dwarf head appears to grow almost directly out of the chest. One cannot see a dwarf's throat due to his beard, and can't see the back of his neck owing to his muscular shoulders.

Stridenvaldr has three, a *Kull* two.[19] Only the *Storvaldr* wears a plume of all black.

skyðð

The shield is at the heart of a modern military dwarf army and has been refined over many centuries, even incorporating a philosophy of dependency between dwarves. It is this approach to shared protection that strengthens the bonds of our oaths and the kinship between all dwarven warriors.

The shield itself is wooden and rectangular, made to a

---

19 Sundin often wore the *hjälm* he bought at Voss Traish. It was that of a *Hojta-dirigent* and never failed to earn dark looks from the dwarves of Voss Kilda (where he now serves). I think he just enjoyed winding up the other soldiers, but there was an element of challenge to wearing such a *hjälm*. Sundin saw fit to have a Voss Traish-style helmet made for me and presented it to me before I left.

prescribed three and a half feet in length and two and a half feet wide. The edges are girded with iron, and more of the same runs in three bands across the shield's face. In addition to this, iron studs are driven through the wood. It is a heavy piece of equipment, but one that has revolutionised our approach to warfare, making us a formidable problem for our enemies.

The shield is strapped to the forearm, which helps bear the burden. A handle on the inside helps the bearer direct the face of the *skydd* towards the direction of attack. Although capable of soaking up a lot of punishment, the *skydd* is not an item you should expect to last the duration of a battle.[20] The iron used in the construction can be salvaged and reforged, then attached to new wood.

Twenty dwarves arranged in five rows of four can form a near impervious box, as mentioned in Chapter 3. Those dwarves at the centre hold their shields over their heads, forming a roof, or top side to the box, while those at the front lock shields to create an intimidating wall of iron and wood. The sides of this formation are the most vulnerable points, so do not become overconfident.

20 The *skydd* is a work of considerable pride among the dwarves. They are effectively mass-produced and bear little or no ornamentation whatsoever, as benefits this very no-nonsense race. A dwarf who loses his shield in battle is said to 'have hit the *skydds*'.

6

ᴅWARVEN EQUIPMENT

'The elves pull magic out of the air, as if it were a gift of the winds, or the light itself. Such ginning is not to be trusted. Put your faith in solid dwarven artifice instead, I say.'

Striden-dirigent Sundin Hallestøm in conversation
after witnessing a minor supplication.[1]

It is important to note that no dwarf with a beard longer than his fist holds any truck with magic. All conjurations are works of deception. However, there are exceptions: enchantments worked into objects imbue those items with power; such items include the Auroch Belts, the *huldurlantern* and various *krona*.

---

1 A supplication is a prayer of sorts to any of the stars of the elves. These celestial beings then bestow a small portion of their power to grant the wish of the petitioner. You can read more about this in Chapter 8: *Aelfir* Arcana in *The* Aelfir *Art of War*.

the Auroch Belts

Long ago, when the dwarf citadels were but rude dwellings on mountainsides, there lived a thief called Lokiir Eldr-Kron.[2] It was one particularly bitter winter that he found himself alone in the White Maw Mountains. By chance he stumbled into the cave of Menja, a solitary and seldom seen *huldurfolka*. Menja was very tall, like all of her kind, but she differed in that she enjoyed creating objects. Menja had turned her back on building with stone and preferred to work with leather. She had crafted for herself ten rings, leather bands which laced up with gold and silver thread. She wore them on her fingers and thumbs, and as years passed by they gained a fraction of her prodigious strength.

Lokiir stole one of the rings as the *huldurfolka* slept, but the troublesome thief had not planned his escape route. He became trapped in Menja's cavern. The *huldurfolka* woke the next day, searching high and low for the missing ring. When it became clear she would not find it, she set about fashioning another ring from leather, again using gold and silver thread. The following night Lokiir stole another ring, but again he failed to escape the cavern. Menja, true to form, rose the next day and set about creating a replacement for the missing ring. This went on for ten nights. Lokiir stole the last of the

2 Lokiir Eldr-Kron is a popular folk hero. His name means 'fire crown', on account of his red mane of hair. '*Lokiir*' is most easily translated as 'taunting one'. It is a fitting epithet as he managed to insult nearly every male dwarf he exchanged words with. It is for this reason that dwarves don't fully trust their flame-haired kin.

original rings and, using the strength the ten rings gave him, lifted a rock blocking a passageway and finally made his way to freedom.

The trickster made his way back to the citadels and sold five belts to the *Storvaldr*. Menja's rings were too big for their fingers, but Lokiir persuaded the kings to wear them as girdles. These belts of auroch leather conferred great strength on the wearer. Only the belt sold to the king of Voss Traish was different, imbuing the wearer with great wisdom.[3]

A king outfitted in such a belt can wield a weapon many times his size and cleave through enemies with ease. King Berigunn the Furious famously punched an elf steed unconscious and beat the elven rider to death with his bare hands while wearing his Auroch Belt.

huldurLantern

The dwarves first encountered the Umber Wraiths in the years following the destruction of the human towns Al Silv and Freed. The Wraiths had the odds stacked in their favour: underground and deep in shadow, they were all but untouchable. Simple torches and lantern light went some way to warding off these fell spirits, but our desperation increased as more of our kin were taken in their sleep.

It was after the first wave of casualties that we

3 Lokiir Eldr-Kron maintained this belt was taken from the thumb of Menja, and it is for this reason dwarves are obsessed with the idea that wisdom resides in one's thumb. Some dwarves even suck their thumb when they are deep in thought. It also common to see dwarves biting their thumbs by way of insult, meaning 'you have no wisdom'.

implored the *huldurfolka* to help us. The *huldurfolka* possess a wisdom that is difficult to aptly describe. They are so in tune with the earth and their surroundings that they see through all *ginning* and subterfuge. No thief apart from Lokiir Eldr-Kron has ever sneaked up on one of these ancient beings.

A dwarf by the name of Rakh Vasskniv hit upon the idea of using enchanted candles. The candles were blessed by the *huldurfolka*, who bestowed a measure of their deep insight into the wax and wick. As the shadow war dragged on, candles alone were abandoned. The *huldurfolka* fashioned silver lanterns, each the size of a *hjälm* within which the candles were set. These lanterns shed a light that renders the Umber Wraiths corporeal, which in turn means they are vulnerable to our weapons. Many citadels feature a *huldurlantern* hanging above the main gate as a matter of course. Smaller, more portable versions have been created over time, and are much sought after.

KRONA

The most famous *krona* was the Kall Krona, the theft of which became the catalyst for the dwarven uprising. The Kall Krona is made of iron and coated in gold, inlaid with diamonds and other pale stones. The Kall Krona confers protection against heat upon the wearer. This is how Odniir Dwarf-Father escaped being burnt alive by Brutenmakt's raging breath. The Kall Krona exists to this day, and is worn by the king of Voss Kilda. Each of the dwarven kings have their own crown, and each of them has unique properties.

The Krona of Century Falls was created by the Great Drake known as Rakhyvel. This krona is not made of metal, but of dark and gleaming granite. When a word is spoken, the wearer and those in his retinue undergo a startling transformation. Each dwarf grows heavy and their skin turns to stone. Those affected are all but impervious to the weapons of our enemies. Some call this the Huldurfolka Krona.

The dwarves of Voss Drun have a *krona* taken from the Great Drake named Frosthatar. The *krona* is known to all as the Frost Halo, for it sheds an unwavering, white light all around. This light is extremely useful for battles beneath the ground. In addition, the light from the Frost Halo reveals Umber Wraiths, rendering them vulnerable to attacks from mundane weapons. The light that falls on these fell spirits burns them.

The Krona of Voss Colg is not a *krona* at all, but a *hjälm*. The helmet is made to look like the head of a Great Drake, and is thought to be sculpted by a dwarf in the image of Raseri the Unclean.[4] Raseri imbued the *hjälm* with the ability to emit fire, although this can be extremely taxing for the wearer. The kings of Voss Colg have always been very keen to lead their troops, and the number of goblins incinerated by Raseri's *hjälm* defies counting.

The *krona* of Voss Jur differs from every other krona in Nedanförvärld. This *krona* was not stolen from a Great Drake, but was instead created by the *huldurfolka* Bestla, after the battle of Scarlet Fang Pass. The *krona*, often called Bestla's Mercy, radiates waves of calm. The king

---

4 Raseri the Unclean has several names, including 'the mad', 'the furious' and 'the petulant'. Despite his shortcomings, which are many, he is known to craft a great many objects, which are in turn stolen by adventurers and redistributed. Some even find homes in human lands; others have been stolen by orcs.

may command the *krona* to release a pulse of healing energy that mends the flesh and bones of injured dwarves nearby.

Over the years other dwarves had dared to re-enter the halls of the Great Drakes. These foolhardy and reckless adventurers have often sought little more than to fill their pockets with bright gold before the drake awakens. Some have returned with a crown, which they sell to the *Storvaldr* in exchange for vast wealth.[5]

ONAGER

The onager has been largely set aside in favour of the ballista in recent centuries, but some remain, and their usefulness should not be overlooked. The onager launches a stone projectile from a sling, which is attached to an arm. The arm sweeps forward via a system of twisted ropes. The torsion is provided by a windlass, operated by two or three dwarves who crew the weapon.

The frame of the onager is made from oak, with four small wheels attached to it for ease of deployment. Two ponies are often hitched directly to the weapon itself in order to transport it to where it is needed.

The onager is less accurate than the ballista, although it does tend to cause massive head wounds, break ribs and crush limbs. The stone projectiles can render even

5 There is popular dwarf pipe dream that through managing to steal an object of great value from a drake, they might be able to retire in luxury. Most of these 'adventuring dwarves' never make quite as much money as they hope. They settle for opening taverns, where they regale their patrons with tales of their travels. Many dwarves set out, never to be seen again, but no one speaks of this.

heavily armoured troops injured or dead. It is best to have three of these weapons acting in concert, targeting formations of troops as one. Attacks of this nature are demoralising in the extreme for most enemy troops, but inconsequential to *akuun*.

BALLISTA

The dwarf ballista takes many forms, and varies in construction from citadel to citadel. I will write in broad terms about the ballistae used at Voss Kilda.

The weapon fires a projectile by means of two torsion levers. The weapon is made from wood and it is possible for engineers to construct a ballista while on campaign. Initially many dwarves used rounded stones, or shot, as ammunition. This is fine against lightly armoured goblins or regular orc warriors, but less devastating against armoured orcs and the implacable *akuun*.

Steel-tipped spears, sometimes called javelins, are the

preferred ammunition in recent times. A javelin can strike through many bodies at once, which is perfect for packed concentrations of troops, such as those entering a dwarf citadel or a mountain pass. The javelin also punctures the tough hides of *akuun*. Once wounded, the *akuun* will spend many moments trying to draw the shaft out of his body. *Akunn* ignoring the javelin will suffer reduced mobility.

You will want to deploy your ballistae on higher ground during open warfare. This allows you to fire over the heads of friendly troops.[6] The higher ground will also afford you a better vantage point, so you can pick your targets according to priority. *Akuun*, shamans, orc elites and their *Khagan* are all worthy targets meriting your full attention.

VISUNÐR HORN

The visundr horn is hollowed out and a smooth opening is made at the pointed end.[7] They are lacquered and varnished and often banded with iron to make them hardier. These horns are given to each *Striden-dirigent*, and the soldiers under his command soon develop a keen ear for that horn's unique sound. Three blasts of the horn indicate the soldiers should charge; two blasts indicate

---

6 Surely it can't be that difficult?

7 Never was there a more unmusical instrument possessed by any of the sentient races that have ever walked the face of Nedanförvärld. The orcs at least stick to drums and have a sense of rhythm. The horns of the dwarves are mighty flatulent things, dull in tone and grating on the nerves, especially first thing in the morning.

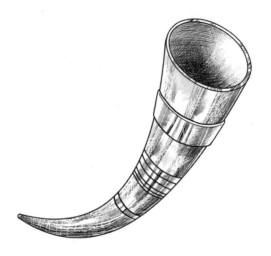

the *trupp* should hold their position. A single blast indicates that the dwarves should form up and begin a fighting retreat.[8]

PENDANTS

While we dwarves are leery of spells we possess a deep affinity with the land, often attributing powers to particular types of stones or minerals. These powers, or resonances, are subtle, but many dwarves would swear an oath to their effectiveness. So it is that dwarves wear pendants. There are far too many to list, so I shall only mention those best suited to the battlefield.

Haematite is perhaps the most popular of dwarven pendants. This mineral is often worked into arrowhead-shaped icons. The black stone has a metallic finish and is

8 Once the dwarves set foot on the field of battle they are absolutely committed. There is no surrender and 'no running away like those beardless humans'.

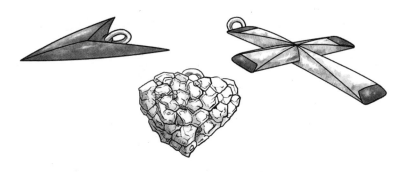

said to protect its wearer from infected wounds. It enhances willpower and optimism, and is thought to give minor protection from magical attacks. This is a common pendant because it is so cheap to make.

Jade is the rarest of pendants among the dwarves, and is valued for the qualities of longevity, wisdom and fortification against poisons. It is particularly favoured by *Förbinda*, who require the stone's unique gifts to carry out their difficult tasks. These pendants come in the form of a cross and the end of each arm is finished in polished iron.

Amethyst pendants are believed to protect the wearer from Umbral attacks, either magical or physical in nature. These pendants were very popular during the Shadow War, but are seen less frequently now. They often come as heart-shaped pendants, or as a stylised eye. Many are handed down from mother to daughter.[9]

Dwarves are not optimistic by nature. They often overcome despair only through the agency of fury. It is not

9 Male dwarves are less inclined to wear amethyst pendants. It is the commonly held view they are 'a bit elfy', which is to say effeminate and ineffective. I myself wear one, happily accepting any protection I can acquire from the clutches of the Umbral Wraiths.

unheard of for some dwarves to lose hope, despite the many tales of heroism told in our halls. Some dwarves wear tourmaline pendants to lift their spirits, even kissing the stones before battle and claiming they are lucky.

OTHER EQUIPMENT

Any dwarf with even half a beard will not leave the confines of his citadel without a good length of sturdy rope (usually thirty feet, sometimes sixty), a grappling hook, some pitons and climbing spikes for his boots. This collection is commonly called the 'Adventuring Kit'.

7

TERRAIN OF THE DWARVES

*'I'd rather be on top of a mountain than underneath it.
Cold I can cope with, darkness and cave-ins less so.'*

Elf scout Suhel Shraykh-Maen in conversation with *Striden-dirigent*
Sundin Hallestøm at the Battle of Scarlet Fang Pass.[1]

Fighting on mountain terrain is notoriously difficult.
Mobility is hampered, footing is questionable, and
all conventional texts on warfare aren't worth the vellum
they're scribed on. Dwarves do not fight on mountainsides out of choice, but out of necessity. A *Stridenvaldr*
should always lead his soldiers to level ground wherever
possible. It is rare that a large-scale battle will take place
on the mountainside; you will most likely be fighting
skirmishes. As such, the following notes are for individual

---

1 Suhel Shraykh-Maen is something of a legend among the elves, managing
both the mantle of outcast and saviour. You can read more about her
exploits in Chapter 9 of this volume.

soldiers, rather than unit-to-unit fighting. *Vandatrupp* and adventuring dwarves might also find the following chapter useful.[2]

hIGhER GROUND[3]

Dwarves will benefit from the advantage of higher ground during an engagement. An opponent running uphill will quickly tire, while those adopting a more casual pace will expose themselves to being cut down by crossbows. This is a rare opportunity for dwarves to fight their enemies face to face, even enjoying a height advantage over goblins, depending on the gradient of the terrain. Enemies carrying shields will not suffer much disadvantage, but those without will have a harder time fighting up the slope. Be wary of those armed with spears; the reach and the angle of attack have cost many over-confident dwarves their lives.

2 Dwarves take a dim view of adventuring, claiming it is neglecting one's duties in the citadel; failing to be present to defend one's kin and king. Adventurers are held in little more esteem than *sperasska*, and are generally considered to be 'bloody nuisances waiting for a chance to become *skulda*'. A slightly different version emerges with the application of three to four flagons of ale. Most dwarves are consumed with the need to retell 'the time we nipped out for a little adventure'. Most dwarves carry around keepsakes of the time they went looking for trouble. There is a nostalgic yearning that fills a dwarf's voice when he recounts his apparently 'epic' quest, or quests in some cases. It is my understanding that these tales become embellished with time and application of the aforementioned ale.

3 This passage barely warrants being in the book, but it's not every day a dwarf gets to look down his nose at an opponent. Unless his foe is dead, or lying on the floor with broken knees, which is much more likely.

ROCK SLIÐES

The mountain can spell an untimely end for the unwary and disturbances can unleash a torrent of stones ranging from mere pebbles to boulders larger than a pony. Many dwarves tie themselves to each other with rope at intervals of fifteen feet. It is unlikely the whole *trupp* will be affected by the rock slide, so those retaining their footing will need to work hard to keep their kin safe from falling further.

Rock slides can also be used against the enemy. While the preparation requires backbreaking work, the results are spectacular. Arranging the stones above a pass or known path across the mountainside will offer the chance to strike an enemy while he is preoccupied with the terrain. Survivors will be torn between looking for those swept away by the rock slide or advancing up the mountain to ensure the attackers don't unleash yet more stones on their position. Any survivors can also be picked off with crossbows.

Goblins have also become fond of this tactic in the last century, using it whenever possible against dwarves across Nedanförvärld. Be warned. Their ambition outmatches their talent, but even a small rock slide gives an ambushing opponent an edge.

WİNÐ FAST

Wind Fast is a term many dwarves like to use when defending their mountain homes. It's rare that a dwarf speaks kindly of the wind – cold draughts find their way into the deepest halls, and unnatural breezes presage the arrival of Umber Wraiths. Winds tend to be stronger at greater altitude, and this makes the life of a bowman especially difficult on the mountain side. It can affect all warriors – yours and the enemy's. Remember that elves seldom fire directly on the battlefield, but instead target units with indirect shooting. The mountainside requires a more considered approach, as such engagements are skirmishes; this is when the skill of individual archers will be put to the test. The wind can turn aside many shots, but should not be counted on, especially if fighting elves, and they are accompanied by their arcane singers.[4] Orcs,

4 Sundin is, of course, referring to the choirs, or *Riis Maená* of the elves. These singers can imbue allies with arcane abilities, such as unerring accuracy. More information on the *Riis Maená* can be found in *The* Aelfir *Art of War,* also scribed by yours truly.

by contrast, struggle to hit a target at the best of times, and the wind will confound their most careful shooting. The same is also true of crossbow bolts. While they are smaller in length it is not unheard of for them to be gusted aside by high wind.

Mountains require slower and careful movement, meaning targets can be picked off as they seek safe passage through the rocks. This is the way *vandatrupp* neutralise small units of inquisitive orcs. Goblins are well acquainted with this tactic and flee at the first sign of trouble unless they have a distinct advantage of numbers.

CAVES

Caves are just as likely to work against you as they are for you. Countless *vaetiir* make their homes in the mountains, lying in wait for unwary mortals to confound, bewitch and, ultimately, murder. Caves featuring underground lakes or rivers will be home to the dreaded *nockiir*. Avoid these places by all means possible, unless you're an empty-headed adventurer, in which case you'll undoubtedly seek them out to enable subsequent bragging. Larger caves are home to entire tribes of goblins, and *akuun* have been known to hibernate inside over winter.[5] It is said the

---

5 The word 'cave' can prove misleading. An original cave is usually expanded, often by dwarven miners, but sometimes by goblins who need more space. Over the centuries these humble caves have become elaborate networks of corridors and halls inside the mountains. Young dwarves often decide to raid these small settlements to ease the boredom of citadel living, and earn themselves some goblin treasure. Goblins are not unlike magpies in that they enjoy shiny things, and there is usually something of note worth plundering at the end of an adventure.

Ruiirmaidens themselves occupy a cave near Century Falls.[6]

While caves seem to provide an opportunity for rest and shelter, they rarely bring much of either. Quick-witted goblins are known to set fires at the cave mouth, choking sheltering dwarves with smoke, attacking them as they stumble out into daylight. Other goblins cause landslides to cover the cave mouth, trapping the dwarves inside, leading to a slow death by starvation. Naturally, if your *trupp* or companions need to rest in a cave you should set reliable look-outs. Dwarven maps constantly seek to record new cave locations and make note of the last known inhabitants.[7] Subterranean caves, or caverns, belong to dwarves as a matter of birthright. We tend to ignore goblins who occupy caves above ground level, but all caverns, chasms and caves beneath the ground belong to us.[8]

6 Dwarves full of ambition and aspiration seek out the Ruiirmaidens for some clue to their futures. While their gift of foretelling is strong, the Ruiirmaidens are not above drowning the weak or the ill-mannered. It is said Osjälviska Storkrona sought their prophecy before his coronation. He was never seen again.

7 Dwarf cartographers are some of the wealthiest dwarves in any given citadel. Dwarves put a great deal of store in preparation, and maps are just another facet of preparing for a journey. The map makers pay handsomely for information on caves and the creatures inhabiting them. They in turn share this information with other map makers in their guild. It is said the Dwarven Guild of Meticulous Cartography is a better intelligence network than any other. When I asked the Guild Master if this were true, he declined to comment and tried to sell me a map for three times what it was worth.

8 When a non-dwarf is found below ground without a dwarf escort it is assumed he is a spy. At that point things become very difficult, as challenging dwarf assumptions is not unlike pulling teeth. Only less fun. I once spent an entire evening explaining I wasn't the vanguard for an invading mercenary army.

passes

Mountain passes are often savagely contested areas of strategic importance. No convoy wants to fight a pitched battle to deliver their supplies and *vandatrupp* dislike being ambushed on supposedly friendly terrain. Passes are the one place on a mountain where large-scale battles are common. Those citadels with sufficient warriors may post garrisons to ensure a pass remains in safe hands. These garrisons have a habit of attracting *akuun* and various *vaetiir*, who make the warriors' lives a misery. Soldiers often complain of being little more than bait, and it is a morale-sapping and unpopular duty.[9]

Recapturing an enemy-held pass is a fraught affair. It is best to have *vandatrupp* find another way around to create a distraction from the main convoy or body of troops. When the enemy is drawn out, you should open fire with crossbows. Crossbow units (or individuals) should be positioned on higher ground on each side of the pass, if possible. If the sides of the defile are steep, you will need to place your crossbows in the front rank. Once the enemy is aware of your deployment you should pull those dwarves back quickly and use warriors bearing shields and hammers or axes.

---

9 Those who serve on garrison duty tend to think themselves a cut above their kin in the citadel. These dwarves find it difficult to go back to the militia style of life: five days at work, one day training, one day rest. Dwarves who exhibit this warrior arrogance are said to have 'gone up the bloody mountain', which runs a suitable parallel to the human expression 'getting above oneself'.

bridges

While not part of mountains themselves, bridges over chasms and gorges are important in much the same way passes are. They can shorten a dwarf's journey by many days and are essential for trade between various citadels. Cunning goblins try to goad *akuun* into knocking down our constructions, and while stone bridges are largely indestructible, wooden bridges do suffer. *Akuun* often make their homes beneath bridges, presumably when they can't find a cave to shelter in. It is for this reason wise dwarves take a selection of goats with them on a journey. The goats are sent over the bridge far ahead of the column of soldiers (or the convoy of goods). The sound of goat hooves on the bridge will distract the *akuun*, who will chase after the hapless goats. You won't need too many, three should be sufficient. Sometimes avoiding a fight is its own reward.[10]

Engagements across bridges are bitter and bloody affairs. Tradition requires a few volleys of crossbow bolts, followed by an advance of warriors in the Cornerstone formation. The second unit may break formation and hunt down any stragglers once the first formation has broken through the enemy line. Goblins seldom have the resolve to stay and fight when their line is breached, and as yet they have not derived a tactic to counter this. Grey Riders, the wolf-riding goblin elite, may cause

---

10 A peculiar story of three goats crossing a bridge persists in dwarf culture. The last of the three goats manages to toss the troll from the bridge with his horns. I'm not aware of any goats that grow this large, and doubt even an auroch or visundr could manage this feat of strength.

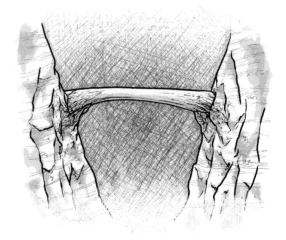

problems and are usually held back in reserve. Spears are needed to ward off the attacks of these light cavalry.

Ruszalkai have also been known to linger near bridges, enchanting and seducing lone travellers before drowning them. They have the ability to change the surrounding landscape, and even the most experienced trackers have become lost when caught up in such *ginning*.[11] The weak-willed are also likely to walk off the bridge, falling to their deaths. Only foolhardy dwarves make a journey across the mountains without companions.

11 Dwarves insist that it was a *Ruszalkai* that led Killi Berigunn from his intended course from Voss Kilda to Voss Traish. His subsequent journey led him onto the mountains of Korlahsia, where he was slain by the elves. It is possible he just got lost, but I don't advise making this suggestion to dwarves, who still lament the siege of Korlahsia and the 'murder' of one of their nobles.

ROPE BRIDGES

Rope bridges are made by idiots. You have no one to blame but yourself if you get halfway across only to find a goblin sawing through the handrail.[12] Only *vandatrupp* use rope bridges with any frequency, and then only as a temporary measure (and a last resort). A cunning *vandatrupp* will collapse the bridge after the squad have passed over, making it difficult or impossible for any enemies to follow.

WINTER

While dwarves are the hardiest of creatures and do not shirk bad weather or difficult quests, it is highly questionable to set out in the depths of winter. Visibility is dramatically reduced, footing is treacherous, and familiar landmarks are obscured by snow or fog, hampering navigation. Even seasoned *vandatrupp* struggle to journey through the mountains at this time of year. Large formations of troops should avoid travelling the mountains at all, opting instead for a route across kinder terrain or waiting until spring.

---

12 Dwarves are obsessed with 'making things to last'. Wood, while useful, burns or rots. Stone on the other hand is infinitely more durable. A bridge made out of rope and wood offends the dwarf's meticulous attention to craftsmanship and permanence.

8

UNDER SIEGE

*'It takes three months to get the necessary equipment
and supplies together to prosecute a siege. Anyone
who says different is looking for a quick death or
is working for the enemy. Probably both.'*

Striden-dirigent Sundin Hallestøm on the subject
of the siege of Korlahsia.

Dwarves are attuned to sieges by their very nature.
Like the magma and clay we were fashioned from,
there is something fiery and intractable about us. But clay
can be brittle once fired, and so it is with sieges. Every
battle has a break point, and sieges are no different. These
conflicts hinge on three concepts: the resilience of the
fortifications; the preparedness of the attackers; and the
morale of the defenders.

Dwarves spend much of their time building and
defending fortifications, and have enjoyed centuries to
perfect both. Over time the five citadels have designed

gatehouses, added buttresses, and raised lofty towers. Concealed doors lead to secret passages, and stout bridges span deep chasms. Chemical mixtures have been crafted and tactics developed to wear down our opponents. Consider the shield, a portable defence, more evidence of our longstanding tradition of reinforcement and protection. However, it would be folly to assume that sieges are the sole domain of dwarves. The elves too are tenacious opponents, as illustrated at Korlahsia, the City of the Dead.

the citadel gates

Every citadel features one main entrance: a large and decorative set of doors meant to impress visitors and add to the glory of the king who resides there. The main doors are set into the side of the mountain itself. Designs differ, but many feature a tower, called *övervetta*, on each side of the entrance. These *övervetta* act as platforms for dwarves with crossbows. It is from these vantage points that we can deter enemy scouts and soften up larger formations of troops. The flat roof of the *övervetta* is home to a ballista. These weapons are given the express order to take down larger targets, such as *akuun*, or if the worst were to happen, the Great Drakes.[1]

The exterior doors are intimidating to those who are

---

1 The dwarves still live in fear that their previous masters will return to rain fire on them. There are few adequate defences against a dragon, and dwarf inventors usually have one project that is preoccupied with dealing with the winged terrors. It's not dissimilar to those human astronomers who worry about comets crashing into their towns. If such an event did happen there'd be almost no defence, short of a miracle.

wavering. The very same doors are also an invitation to any who seek to fall on our blades, wishing to end their days shot down by bolts. It is hoped the main doors will draw our enemies away from lesser portals, which remain hidden through feats of great artifice, or behind waterfalls.

Voss Kilda and Voss Drun also feature an outer wall that extends from the mountain in a semicircle. This wall features a gatehouse of its own, providing a courtyard of sorts where dwarves can marshal the *trupp* and rally if the walls are taken.

It stands to reason that enemy soldiers bearing ladders should be targeted first, lest they bring their equipment within range and scale the wall. The defence of the outer wall is a shocking and harrowing affair. Enemy missiles rain down chaotically, a seething mass of soldiers attempt to break down the doors, and screams of the dying fill the air. Turning back the ladders, or destroying them entirely, is the first in a number of tasks undertaken by those under siege.

Once the outer wall is taken the order will be given to fall back. The dwarves manning the *övervetta* provide crossbow support to those dwarves below until they return to safety behind the outer doors of the citadel. This can be a costly affair, and the order must be given so that dwarves have sufficient time to stay ahead of their enemies.[2]

2 Which is to say they don't really have much of a chance. There are few things slower on the face of Nedanförvärld than a dwarf in plate armour carrying a shield. What the dwarves rely on is the fusillade of crossbow bolts that will distract and kill their enemies, preventing them from hacking down their retreating kin.

FIRE AS A WEAPON

Fire is an implacable weapon, and one that does as much damage to morale as it does to the flesh. No creature that walks and breathes does not fear fire, for it brings a cruel and terrible death. Enemies attacking the doors should be greeted with pitch and fire.[3] Even the most heavily armoured foe becomes a corpse when assailed with burning pitch. The fire inflicted this way is almost impossible to remove and equally difficult to extinguish.

The dwarves of Voss Drun also add sulphur to their mixtures, which has the added effect of blinding enemies and causing breathing problems. Every moment an enemy wastes trying to extinguish the flames, or choking on fumes, is another moment our crossbows can reload and fire. Enemies set alight will blunder into their kin, setting them alight, aiding the defenders. This can undo even the most seasoned veteran, routing entire units. You should not count on the enemy's lack of resolve, simply thank your ancestors on the occasions it happens. Sulphur mixtures have turned the tide of battle many times over the centuries, and it is for this reason that the dwarves of Voss Drun export it to other citadels.[4] These

---

3 Dwarves call these alchemical mixtures *förakt*, which translates as 'disdain'. This naming comes from the tale of when Brutenmakt incinerated five families as punishment for the theft of the Kall Krona. It is said he summoned all his disdain to rid himself of his treacherous subjects. This has cast a long shadow on the dwarf psyche; they regard being burnt in war as a particularly ignoble end.

4 At a hefty mark up, no doubt. Dwarves speak proudly of the bonds of kinship and loyalty, but never miss the opportunity to turn a handsome profit. Dwarves who sell these chemical mixtures can be found easily by the noticeable lack of eyebrows, and in some cases, much shortened beards.

mixtures also suit being added to onager ammunition, but have been known to cause some unfortunate incidents among the siege crews who operate them.[5]

WE WILL FIGHT THEM ON THE CAUSEWAY . . .

The outer doors of every citadel have been broken through at some point, and will undoubtedly be broken through again. This is not a sign of dwarven failure, rather a measure of the enemy's preparedness and determination.[6] The outer doors are just the beginning, and once enemy soldiers gain entrance to the mountain they will find their task becomes that much harder. Goblins, like dwarves, are accustomed to the gloom under our mountains. Orcs, however, do not enjoy the passages and corridors as much, and are prone to become lost, arguing among themselves once doubt sets in.

The outer doors of every citadel lead to a bridge that crosses a deep chasm, called the causeway. On the far side of the bridge is another set of doors, smaller and more reinforced than the outer gates. The bridge itself lies under the range of two galleries; one each side of the causeway. These galleries provide a place for crossbows

5 Note the masterful talent for understatement in this paragraph. 'Unfortunate incident' meaning 'all crew were subsequently burnt to death along with the onager they were operating'. Unfortunate indeed.

6 Dwarves rather prefer it when the enemy breaches the outer doors. They consider anything less a 'training exercise'. An enemy that fails to break through the doors is held in contempt by the dwarves, who complain about 'the lack of resolve and planning of a good honest enemy'.

to continue to harass the attackers, just as the *övervetta* did outside. Likewise, the galleries are also home to ballistae, which benefit from targeting a large number of troops packed into a small entrance. They are also essential for killing *akuun*, who can seemingly weather most punishment a dwarf can mete out. Only wounds from five-foot-long javelins give these brutes much cause for concern, and even then it takes repeated firing to bring an *akuun* to its knees.

A gallery is located above the interior gate, and it is from here that more crossbows and burning pitch can be marshalled. The gallery itself features several holes through which these fiery concoctions can be poured. The goblins call these 'murder holes' in their own foul tongue. Using sulphur in the confines of the mountain is to be avoided, lest the dwarves themselves be overcome by the very fumes they are attempting to inflict on their enemies.

Bridges force concentrations of troops, even small numbers of skirmishers, into an area where they can be contained. Chasms, whether they be natural or dwarf-made, are an excellent deterrent for all creatures save giant spiders[7] and tomb blights. The chasm consumes the many corpses that inevitably result from crossing the bridge and advancing into the teeth of the dwarven defences. The best chasms have running water at the bottom, to carry the dead away. The last thing you want

7 Yes, giant spiders. Not merely large spiders, but giant spiders. 'Bloody gargantuan spiders' would be a more suitable epithet. Did I mention how much I hate spiders?

is putrefying bodies spreading diseases on your own front doorstep, so to speak.

The bridges themselves tend to be constructed from a central stone arch. This is called the spine. A large wooden framework overlays the spine, making the bridge wider for carts and wagons.[8] In times of duress the wooden portion of the bridge can be removed, making access narrow and treacherous. Never set fire to the bridge itself, no matter how desperate you are. Doing this risks losing the spine of the bridge, which is costly and time-consuming to replace.

AND IN THE CORRIDORS . . .

All is not lost if the enemy break through the interior doors. While difficult to comprehend, it does happen. It is often the result of a troll being used as a living battering ram. Fortunately goblins have not yet mastered the fell magic that enables orc shamans to control the mighty *akuun*.

Corridor fighting is a desperate and chaotic undertaking; the tactics take one of two forms. When facing goblins, the spearmen give their shields to the dwarves bearing crossbows. These dwarves fire from behind the cover of the shields until the enemy charges into close-quarters fighting. The dwarves in the front rank stow

8 If you think this sounds precarious and is an abandonment of sound architectural dogma, then you would be absolutely right. While dwarf bridges look solid, they appear to stay up largely as a result of the belief the dwarves put in them. I was soundly laughed at when I asked why the bridges lacked a handrail.

their crossbows and lock the shields in an attempt to provide an immovable wall. The dwarves behind them, in the second rank, thrust their spears over the shields, killing the hapless attackers. Most dwarven corridors are built in such a way that three dwarves stood abreast can block the way, provided they have the necessary shields.

This tactic is strengthened further by having a few dwarves armed with axes and hammers waiting at the back. These dwarves can step in to replace any fallen kin if things turn sour, or add support should the goblins break through with weight of numbers.

The second form of this tactic emulates the first, but does away with the crossbows. Here, both ranks are made up of spearmen, with the second rank providing a 'roof' of shields to the front rank. A miniature Cornerstone formation, if you will. This doubles the number of spears protruding from the gaps. This formation only lasts so long, and goblins will inevitably scramble over the top. This is where the third rank proves vital, and it can be made up of any number of dwarves armed with close-quarters weapons, particularly hammers and axes.[9]

---

9 Or just one really surly dwarf with a two-handed axe who was recently ransomed back to his people minus his beard. This sort of dwarf can hold a corridor with very little support.

. . . AND IN THE HALLS

A dwarven hall is the centrepiece of dwarven life. It is where families gather, disputes are settled, laws passed, and feast days celebrated. It is also where warriors muster for war. Some dwarves even practise their skill at arms in these halls, and so it is understandable that a hall should also be fought in.

This is not an ideal situation. If the enemy has penetrated the doors to our family homes we are indeed hard-pressed. However, it is when dwarves are pressed most fiercely that they fight the hardest.

The tables of the great halls should be turned on their sides, giving dwarves with crossbows cover behind which they can reload. It is also helpful to rest the crossbow itself on the edge of the table, as this improves aim. A dwarf behind a feast table armed with a spear is an unwelcome proposition for most enemies. The tables, made of thick wood, and reinforced to bear the weight of our feasts, must be arranged in such a way that leaves no way through unimpeded. Should a gap open in the defences, you should quickly send dwarves with shields. If an enemy has broken through, dwarves equipped in this fashion can push them back with a solid charge. However, if you do not have ample momentum, you may prefer to isolate the enemy from his kin. Do this by filling the hole in the defences and setting warriors on the enemies that have got through.

Many great halls have balconies or galleries, and it is from here you should place the majority of your crossbows. In this way you can bring a great number of ranged weapons to bear on a small area, that area being the doors to the hall itself. This withering rain of crossbow bolts has routed many goblin assaults, stopping scores of orcs in their tracks. The gallery, or balcony, is also a good position for the *Kull* to direct the battle from.

Should an *akuun* enter the hall, then your best hope is to set dwarves armed with two-handed axes upon it. Attack the knees to reduce its mobility, then fall upon the more vulnerable portions of its anatomy, such as armpits, throat and eyes. Tell the dwarves armed with crossbows to aim for the eyes and throat. This should keep any instances of shooting one's own to a minimum due to great difference in height between dwarves and the *akuun*. These creatures do not die quickly, and they always take a score of dwarves with them as they go. Do not be disheartened, but keep up the pressure. Often these creatures fall when all seems lost.

EVACUATION

The womenfolk and youngsters should be sent away the moment the doors of the hall come under attack. Trapdoors leading to winding tunnels, chimneys with rungs worked into the insides, and passages leading to concealed entrances, are all common devices used in dwarven construction.

Evacuation is a last resort, as womenfolk will be forced to lead the youngsters to a location that may not be safe. It is best if they remain in the tunnels until the sounds of fighting in the hall have quietened. In some tragic cases the evacuees have left the safety of the mountain only to be captured, while the warriors inside prevail.

9

ᴄhe baᴛᴛle of scarleᴛ fang pass

An account of the battle of Scarlet Fang Pass,
as recounted by Sundin Hallestøm, who was at that time
the *Hojta-dirigent* of the *Sekund Århundrade, Voss Kilda.*

decade of fear

No war should or needs to last thirty-five years. And
yet Nedanförvärld knew no peace for the best part
of four decades. The elves defended their forests, the
humans stood watch over their towns, and the dwarves
guarded the gates of their citadels. Some dire influence
was directing the orcs, but we could never have guessed
how cunning that intelligence was.

Word had reached us of orc attacks on every citadel,
testing our resolve. The wave of aggression broke on the
shields of dwarves everywhere, then rolled back, threaten-
ing to sweep in again; a maleficent tide. Occasionally
human scouts would reach us bearing fearful tales of two

orc *Khagan* uniting an unprecedented number of tribes on the Kourgaad Plains.

The attacks were not constant, but each year brought a handful of skirmishes. Supply caravans were sacked, many engagements were fought to protect the slow moving convoys. Trade between the citadels dried up as dwarves grew less inclined to risk sending their goods onto the open roads.

I was stationed at Voss Jur at the time. My *Århundrade* had been sent on behalf of King Berigunn II, still chasing the dream of uniting all dwarves as one nation. Seventy-five dwarves sent to sweeten the proposition of joining the 'Union of Dwarven Peoples'. In the end I would lead just a tenth of those dwarves back to their home at Voss Kilda.

DECADE OF SORCERY

The war continued to rage on the Kourgaad Plains: less intense in the foothills of the Bitterfang Mountains, but bloody and dire at the edges of the Great Northern Forest.

Veteran *vandatrupp* returned to Voss Jur with ashen faces. They spoke of a fell voice carried on the western wind. The stoic scouts told us goblins were gathering at Asaan's Abyss, making peace with the few orc tribes that remained in west Nedanförvärld. We were unaware of any charismatic *Khagan* at that time. Asaan himself had crossed the mountains to declare war on the elf High King. The orcs left in the west had been an aimless rabble until now. What eldritch force was uniting the tribes, remaining unseen even to our most experienced scouts?

Attacks increased in their frequency at both Sun Dog Pass and Scarlet Fang Pass, with tribes of goblins passing through unchallenged and unchecked.[1] The dwarves of Voss Colg and Voss Jur were consumed with suspicion as dark shadows haunted the night, often taking guards from their posts and leaving no trace of them. All of this was just a taste of what the following decade would bring.

ÐECAÐE OF AGGRESSION

It was in the third decade that the orcs under *Ur-Khagan* Asaan ceased their predations in the Arendsonn Kingdom. They marched west over the Kourgaad Plains, their attentions fixed more keenly on the elves than ever before. Some of their number still harassed the dwarves of Voss Colg, but, in the main, Voss Jur remained untroubled.

It was towards the end of this decade that the western orcs decided to leave a tribe of goblins in the Scarlet Fang Pass permanently. This provoked great ire in the dwarves of Voss Jur, who were shaken out of their apathy and took to the field. Four *Århundrade* marched out, supported by *vandatrupp*, some three hundred dwarves all told, splendid in their breastplates, the autumnal sun reflecting from steel axe heads.

The goblins caught sight of us and ran forward in

1 Sun Dog Pass draws its name from the goblins who live in that locality. The goblins hammer stout posts into the ground to which they tie their captives. When friends attempt a rescue, the goblins surge from their places of hiding and ambush them. The captives on the posts are called Sun Dogs by the goblins, as they invariably die of thirst, burnt by the hot sun.

mindless fury, gibbering and shrieking as they came. There seemed to be no shadow or overhang that did not harbour these dark-eyed fiends.

We quickly sent for reinforcements.

Many *trupp* formed up behind their shields, offering protection to those that had none. It was not our intent to kill all the goblins, merely to outlast them. How many hours we remained like that, I cannot tell. Those with shields formed a cordon around rises or hillocks, where dwarves with crossbows fired overhead. Aim, release, reload; aim, release, reload. There were no heroic war cries, no call to arms, no rousing speeches, just a few hundred dwarves clinging to their lives as a swarm of hateful goblins swirled around. Crude javelins arced through the air, claiming the unlucky or the unwary. We tithed five lives for every dwarf that fell to the black and rusting blades of the goblins. Soon the ground was littered with broken corpses. The charnel and latrine stench of that battle lived on in my memory long after the wind had seen fit to disperse it.

The reinforcements arrived, the goblins were turned back, fleeing in undisciplined terror. We looked on the faces of our rescuers and saw that the dwarves of Voss Jur had been joined by a squad of human scouts. These weather-worn, mounted men were in turn accompanied by an altogether more curious character.[2]

shraykh-maen's warning

At first we were not sure what it was, but realisation dawned that the creature was an elf, although as hard-eyed and as cold-hearted an elf that ever drew breath. She was a ragged thing, not the soft enchantresses of dwarven fictions. Many were shocked, they had never seen an elf

2 By coincidence I was part of this unit of scouts, who had been charged with bringing a message from Voss Colg to Voss Jur. I am ashamed to say we managed to get lost, but in doing so we stumbled upon the elf 'Shraykh'. Who knows what course the Asaanic War would have taken if this error had not occurred?

before. I was required to still the more impulsive axes among my kin.

The human scouts had found her half dead and in-coherent on the south bank of the Sun Dog river, three days' walk from Voss Colg. Many dwarves were incensed. Was she a sorceress? Had she been sent to sow chaos among us? Was she a spy? Finally she broke her silence, and what she told us was more terrible than any of us dared to imagine.

She called herself Shraykh, telling us she was a member of the dreaded *Drae Adhe*, the elite scouts of the elves. Her band of warriors had ventured to Asaan's Abyss to gain some clue of the evil force waiting in the darkness. They had discovered a powerful Umbral sorcerer called Haelspont, who had gathered the tribes and was intent on sending them to the *Ur-Khagan* Asaan Firebringer.[3] It was her opinion that the reinforcements would aid Asaan's great campaign of extermination of the elves. Starting at Naer Khaeris, the tribes would trek east, destroying Thea Suin and Sia Na Roin, completing the pogrom in Khaershâine. The elves would be hounded at every turn, hunted until the Fuenriis ran red with their blood.

Many dwarves simply shrugged their shoulders at this. It was not their burden to protect a race of near-immortal people they neither knew or cared for. There had been no peaceful contact between dwarf and elf in living memory. Was it any issue of the dwarves if an entire race died at the hands of Asaan Firebringer?

It was at this point my temper slipped its leash.

I explained that it would only be a matter of time until the orcs turned their attention to the dwarves – inevitable once the elves were destroyed. The orcs would not stop until all other living beings on the face of Nedanförvärld were dead. All who heard my words saw the truth in them, even though it grieved them to admit it. Each of us

3 I now know that *Ur-Khagan* Asaan Firebringer was indeed in contact with Haelspont, through his shaman, Ajjall Dogface. This corroborates the account that *Ur-Khagan* Kani Breakspeare recounted during my time among the orc tribes.

realised that the future of the dwarves was inextricably linked to that of the elves.[4]

Shraykh then revealed that Haelspont was planning to lead a number of orc and goblin tribes through the Scarlet Fang Pass. These reinforcements would join Asaan Firebringer's host and march on Naer Khaeris. If we were to give the elves any hope of surviving, we had to prevent those reinforcements from reaching their destination.

the battle of scarlet fang pass

Supplies were brought from the citadel; scores of camp-fires marked our presence in the night. Earthworks were raised at first light and it was noon when we sighted our enemies at the far end of the pass. Spades were quickly abandoned for weapons.

It had begun.

The few *huggtand* among us had sought higher ground, using their crossbows to pick off the approaching rabble. The rest of us waited in the pass itself, a stubborn wall of steel. At first it was little more than practice. Some dwarves began scoring their head counts on the backs of their shields. There was a joyful aspect to the scene, with much back slapping and braggadocio. I stayed apart from the mood of congratulation, my eyes

4 I witnessed this speech by Sundin. It was not a rousing call to arms by any means, nor was it inspirational or rhetoric or coercion. I don't know what it was, but it broke through the stony apathy. Something in the air changed, and when it did I knew that none present would let any orc reach the Kourgaad Plains alive.

fixed on the horizon, anxiety gnawing at me. My fears proved well founded and arrived sevenfold.

The human scouts arrived back with a vague estimate that we had killed barely one-tenth of the goblins, and the rest would be at our throats by dawn. The boisterous cheer fled and I petitioned the various *Kull* to send for reinforcements from the Voss Jur. None listened, of course. Me, a low-born, telling them what to do. Unthinkable. I settled down to a fitful sleep, fearing our doom.

Che SECONO OAY

We were almost overrun on the southern flank in the hours before dawn. Goblins prefer to fight before the sun reaches its zenith. The sky itself was blood red, making the tableau of goblins in front of us all the more terrible. While the northern side of the valley was ably covered by crossbows, the same couldn't be said of its opposite. We fought with axe and hammer, we mashed our shields into their hideous, grinning faces. Swing, cleave, grunt. We settled into the rhythm of it; the stamina of every dwarf taxed to its limit.

A *Stridenvaldr* stumbled into me, his eyes wide with shock. I clasped his shoulder and checked him for wounds. He seemed whole.

'Are you wounded?' I bellowed at him. No response – his mind had fled. 'What's wrong with you?' I pressed.

He pointed at the far end of the pass, mute with horror. Orcs had pressed into the defile, but behind them were the unmistakable hulking silhouettes of *akuun*. I gave the *Stridenvaldr* a nip of whisky from my flask and told him

to get word back to the citadel. I had an idea, but I could only achieve it with his authority. Thank the ancestors he saw the wisdom of what I was about. He set to his task and the battle continued, full of feverish intensity.

There are no words that aptly describe fighting so many goblins, but I will try my best. Such a press of bodies makes a mockery of all warriors, even those of us who are long-trained and hardened by experience. I killed as many goblins with my forehead as I did with my axe. The crush of bodies was so fierce it was only your breastplate that allowed you to draw breath. I recovered a goblin dagger and turned it on the eyes and throats of my enemies, stamping on necks after they had slithered to the ground. All glorious tales of swinging axes and the murderous fall of hammers became redundant. There was nothing showy, or proud or noble about that kind of fighting, just the mindless hooting cries of the goblins and a tangle of limbs, blood-slicked and frantic.[5] The air itself was a hateful din of screeching bats, summoned by the foul *ginning* of their shamans. We fought on, but the southern flank still lacked support from our crossbows. The *Århundrade* fighting there looked fragile. They would not hold much longer.

I never learned the name of the *Stridenvaldr* who carried my recommendation to the citadel, nor did I ever see him again, but I do know that he executed my plans to the letter. The carts used in the trade caravans of Voss Jur were pressed into service for something altogether more useful. They arrived, groaning under the weight of *huggtand* and ballistae, ferrying them to the southern flank, taking them to the foothills. The carts were all pulled by teams of sure-footed mules, who abandoned all pretence of being ornery. The dwarves jumped clear of the carts and took up positions, only too pleased to join the fight. The rain of crossbow bolts

5 Not strictly true. There was also a lot of dwarf cursing. Some of the most elaborate invective I have ever had the good fortune to hear issued from dwarves in the heat of battle.

softened the horde, but there would be a longer wait for the more complex ballistae. Engineers scurried about with tools, setting up the machines with care. The added weight of ranged attacks caused the enemy to falter. Evening approached. The enemy's fervour for carnage abated. No one likes to fight with the sun in their eyes, least of all goblins. The dwarves looked to each other grimly. All our forces were committed to the pass now, none remained to protect Voss Jur. We held here, or the women and youngsters back at the citadel would pay the price for our failure.

The Third Day

Haelspont himself appeared before the sun had seen fit to rise on the third day. He stood among his host, rivalling even the *akuun* in height. We could not see him clearly at first. Enchanted robes of living shadow swirled about him. A pall of bats flapped and screeched over his horned crown. He clasped a gnarled and blackened staff in his right fist. None who saw him dared speak, many of us struggled to draw breath. The orcs and goblins parted reverently, allowing the Umbral sorcerer to stalk closer to our line. My *Århundrade* was in the centre that morning and would pay a steep price once Haelspont had spoken.

The previous day's fighting had been draining and brutal, but the dwarves had clung to the earthworks. They were hardly the dressed-stone defences of a citadel, but had offered us a measure of respite. They were the reason we still remained. Apparently the same thought had occurred to Haelspont.

The Umbral sorcerer had the audacity to venture within range of our crossbows. Those who were not paralysed with terror took their chances. Some bolts he batted away with a deft gesture of his hand, others were lost in the confusion of bats that boiled above him in a frenzy of wings.

None among us clamoured to meet him in combat.

Haelspont raised his staff above his head with both

hands and the air thrummed with unholy energy. We watched transfixed, not knowing what would come next. The sorcerer slammed his staff into the packed earth and gave a wordless shout. It was as if twenty voices called out at once, each more discordant than the last. The dwarves fell on their faces, clutching their hands to their heads. Long moments passed as we lay there, some bleeding from nose and ears.

I don't remember falling, only that I looked up as an agonised groan shuddered through the earth beneath me. When the shaking had stopped, the entire dwarf army was in disarray, many buried in the very earthworks that had kept them alive the previous day. The orcs and goblins surged forward, like a howling pack of dogs. Haelspont dropped into cover as the sun came up, leaving the work of defeating the dwarves to his minions. I looked around in desperation for my kin, but many had been swallowed by fissures that had opened in the ground. Others struggled to free themselves from rockslides; they were easy prey when the goblins found them. I gathered together those dwarves from Voss Kilda that I could find, ordering them back from the confusion. The remaining dwarves despaired, giving ground foot by foot, weeping into their beards for the loss of sons and fathers and grandfathers.

And then the weapon of the enemy began to claim its own.

The goblins, nimble and sharp-eyed, traversed the shattered ground with ease. They called out with gleeful taunts and hopped and leaped over the gaping wounds in the earth. The orcs by contrast were not so agile. Many were weighed down with heavy armour. The ground beneath them collapsed, consigning them to newly opened caves many feet below. These armoured orcs disappeared from view, never to be seen again. The orcs at the back of the army pressed forward, all too keen to join the fight, pushing those at the front towards the rent and ruptured ground. It had been Haelspont's plan to break through with his most elite and heavily armoured orcs. Few now remained.

The dwarves had regained both their feet and their resolve during the chaos. We gave thanks to our ancestors and promised vengeance.

haelspont's rage

Haelspont raged and hissed, hiding from the sun beneath a restless cloud of bats. The difficult ground was an impediment to the orcs, who were picked off by our crossbows. Some of us hoped that this was the turning point of the battle, hopes that were dashed when we saw the trolls shambling forward. Haelspont, in his fury, had unleashed his most fearsome warriors. I counted perhaps a score of the *akuun*, some bearing crude clubs made from small trees. I had never seen so many foul creatures gathered together in one place. My heart turned to lead.

The ballistae did their part, of this there is no question. I saw one great beast take no less than three steel-tipped javelins, and still it came at us, bellowing and grunting. Entire *trupp* were shattered and broken as they attempted to kill the towering beasts. Dwarf bodies were flung into the air. Crossbow bolts were but minor irritations to creatures like these. The ballistae continued to target the *akuun*; one died spectacularly with a shaft through its eye. The dwarves gave up a throaty cheer, before realising that another score of *akuun* had moved up behind the first. Two score of *akuun*. I had naively hoped there were not that many in the whole Nedanförvärld.

The Centre Cannot Hold

Haelspont's quake had dire consequences for his battle plans. The tortured ground had already claimed his elite orc soldiers, and now he would see the full extent of his folly. There are creatures in Nedanförvärld who are more attuned with the rocks and earth than even we dwarves, and they had been greatly angered by Haelspont's destructive *ginning*. They came from the deep places where not even dwarves venture, from a darkness more total than an eclipse. They came, and even the *akuun* were lost in the great shadows that fell on the land.

It was of course common knowledge that Bestla, the most kind and patient of all *huldurfolka*, slept beneath Voss Jur. That Ganger had been nearby too was a boon. Ganger, by contrast, was not a kind or patient *huldurfolka*. The anger of his dismissal by the Great Drakes burnt as hot in his veins as magma. Some dwarves claimed steam escaped from his mouth and nose, like a beard of white vapour.

The remaining orcs and goblins fled, preferring to risk the wrath of Haelspont himself than face two *huldurfolka*. Ganger raised one foot and stamped an *akuun* flat into mud, then let out a roar that was heard in Voss Colg.

I ran to the foothills in the north and exhorted the ballistae to resume their work. What followed was both titanic and terrible. The *akuun*, who are too stupid to experience fear, stood their ground, trying to claw and bite at living rock. The dwarves cheered and screamed themselves hoarse, and the ballistae struck again and again. Bestla and Ganger reaped a grim harvest. Bestla pulverised skulls beneath her granite fists; she flung *akuun* at the fleeing orcs. Few survive having an *akuun* corpse landing on them. Ganger made an example of the *akuun* that will haunt the nightmares of orcs for decades to come. One great hand would grasp the head and shoulders of an *akuun*, the other the hips. Next would come a sickening pause, and then the troll would be flung aside as two ragged parts, raining entrails as they fell. The carnage was total, the Scarlet Fang Pass remained ours, or so we thought.

HAELSPONT'S RETURN

We had hoped the Umbral sorcerer would admit defeat upon seeing his *akuun* destroyed, and flee back to the poisonous abyss. But once again he stalked forward, and once again he raised his staff, the source of his destructive power. So great was his fury, so intense his desperation, that he came forth without summoning his cloud of bats. The sun fell on the Umbral sorcerer, revealing the true extent of his evil, rendering him solid in the light. Umber Wraiths can only avoid mortal wounds while in shadow and darkness.

It was as Haelspont raised his staff that I spotted her. She had remained conspicuously absent for the duration of the battle, and in truth I had expected little more. My prejudices made me all too keen to suppose the elf had fled, happy to let us die for her cause.

She ran forward with a quickness that was breathtaking. All around me the dwarves were clasping their hands to their ears, fearing the profane din that would presage another quake. Shraykh, last *Drae Adhe* in all the Scarlet Fang Mountains, ran forward. In her hands she clasped a great spear, one of the many ballista shafts that now littered the battlefield.

Haelspont was lifted off his feet, the tip pushing through his back and emerging from his breast. He coughed, smoke and shadow escaping his maw. A look of disbelief crossed his twisted features. We all held our breath.

A fierce tremor overtook the Umbral sorcerer, who turned to look on the face of his attacker. Suhel Shraykh-Maen stared into the face of evil, and was struck down. Haelspont lashed out, back-handing the elf to ground. There followed long painful seconds as he removed the spear from his breast. We watched aghast.

And then he faded from view like smoke caught on a breeze.

I would like to think that Shraykh's sacrifice destroyed the sorcerer, but I fear he will one day rise again from Asaan's Abyss.

As for the dwarves, we buried our dead, and the months and years that followed were not happy ones. I took the remaining dwarves in my command back to Voss Kilda, praying to my ancestors that we had done enough to help bring an end to the Asaanic War.

10

A SUMMARY OF THE DWARVES

BY SEBASTIAN VENGHAUS

My colleagues,

The dwarves of Naer Evain are a suspicious folk, slow to make bonds of friendship and all too keen to nurse old grudges and nurture new slights. Their skill at arms and deep affinity for stone and metal is matched only by their distrust for magic. Their great pride and tenacity, while an asset, is also the reason they remain so isolated from the other races. Dwarven artifice is meticulous and made to stand the test of time, but so too are the internecine squabbles that occur between the great citadels. If the dwarves were ever to align their interests, they would undoubtedly become one of the great powers, if not the great power of Naer Evain.

It was while living among these proud people that I came to understand that the *dvergiir* are shaped by the environment they thrive in. The snow-clad mountains and misty foothills are rife with dangers for the unseasoned traveller. Swamp-dwelling Ruszalkai attempt to confuse and waylay those who stray into their domains, while the *Vodyniir* make the lives of dwarf fishermen difficult and unreasonable. Then there are the mighty nockiir – vast water serpents capable of devouring livestock, easily the match of any stout warrior.[1] Dwarven tales abound of the Ruiirmaidens, and how they foretell dire events. Some dwarf warriors, keen to seek the Ruiirmaidens counsel, fall in love with these enigmatic water spirits and never return to their citadels. Meanwhile, deep below the ground itself, are the *huldurfolka,* great beings of living stone who must be treated with the utmost respect. In many ways the dwarves are beset on every side by mischievous water spirits, known collectively as *vaetiir.* If the elves live in harmony with the land, then the dwarves in contrast are surely at war with it. Many times during my stay I listened to dwarves describing themselves as 'under siege' from the world outside their great underground citadels. This is not merely a figure of speech, but their way of life.

The goblins have devoted their entire existence to usurping the dwarves in their great halls. Even now, goblin tribes crave to bring the great families to their knees, despoiling their honour and slaying their young. While fewer in number, the *akuun* are no lesser a threat.

1 The word 'knucker' is derived from the dwarven word nockiir. Many human children in Hoim are told by their parents that a knucker will come for them if they refuse to behave. Dwarf children have real cause to be scared, as five or six inevitably disappear due to the predations of the water serpents each year.

The cave trolls are capable of terrible acts of destruction when feral, when under the control of a shaman they are nothing less than living siege engines. The *dvergiir* are truly a race under constant threat. This mindset of eternal siege makes the dwarves a difficult race to become allies with, but become allies with them we must.

The dwarves are not only shaped by their environment, but by their oldest and most-revered myths. I learned that every dwarf is taught from a young age that the original *dvergiir* were made by the Great Drakes. Such a thing seems ridiculous to learned men, but the dwarves insist that the Great Drakes needed new minions after the golems, or *huldurfolka*, proved to be too slow. Until this point, they explain, the *huldurfolka* had built great subterranean halls for the drakes, but they proved too large and too ponderous for simple errands once the construction was finished. The myths describe the Great Drakes making dwarves from clay, but during the process some magma was accidentally added to the mix. This, the dwarves say, is where they gain their great temper. Their pride comes from the drakes themselves, and perhaps their love of gold also.

The dwarves of ancient times served the Great Drakes for one hundred years and did so without gratitude from the fiery serpents. So profound was the disdain of the Great Drakes for the dwarves that they forgot to create any women. This was devastating for the dwarves. When the Great Drakes did attempt to correct their folly it was to little gain. They created just a few dozen women, who, naturally, were hotly fought for. This still holds true to this day, where female dwarves can represent anything from a third to just a quarter of a citadel's adult population.

Dwarven daughters are one of the few things more precious to dwarf lords than gold.[2]

Eventually, after a long service that was largely unappreciated by the Great Drakes, the dwarves rebelled, following in the example of Odniir Dwarf-Father, and the group he'd freed from Brutenmakt. All the dwarves cast off their duties and made lives for themselves in the world above. Many did not last the first summer. The Great Drakes attacked their creations and made the raising of buildings impossible. They came by night, and day by day, they swallowed dwarves whole or ripped them apart. There was nothing the Great Drakes would not do to punish their rebellious children. The dwarves despaired and were nearly extinguished. At last, fortune smiled upon the stout folk and a decade of unusually bitter winters forced the Great Drakes to hibernate inside the volcanoes they are so fond of. They sleep there still, according to dwarf tales at least.[3]

Their myths cast a long shadow over the dwarves, who, in lieu of a beneficial creator, have turned to ancestor worship. The bonds between dwarf families are strong, their concept of duty vast, and their refusal to betray their kin without question. I could not, however, help

2 There is an idea among the other races that dwarf women have beards, and dwarf men are embarrassed by their women folk. This is simply not true. The reason dwarf women are so rarely seen in public is because they are guarded zealously.

3 Rumours persist that a Great Drake woke and joined the fray at the battle of Century Falls, but theories exist that the great winged creature seen was no more than a figment conjured by the Umber Wraith sorcerers. I for one am unconvinced.

noticing the dwarves feel somewhat lost in the world, and as a result have become self-reliant and independent almost to a fault.

There is also, dare I say, an element of self-pity in the *dvergiir*. Bad enough they should struggle to populate their grand citadels with future generations, but there is a deeper malaise. Thousands of years later they still feel Storgunn's[4] betrayal all too keenly. While they cherish the gifts of knowledge Storgunn gave them, they are all too aware of the advantages possessed by the forest-dwelling elves. The elves outlive them, outpace them, and can summon miracles from the heavens. Add to this the elves' talent for mockery and sarcasm, and the mix becomes a bitter one. The dwarves enjoy humour only when it is not at their expense. It would serve both sides well if these ancient cultures could set aside their differences, but I fear they are too engrossed in centuries-old grievances and unpaid debts.

So, it falls to the humans to attempt to overcome the dwarven misgivings of allying themselves with other races. It is true enough that the dwarves depend on human agriculture, and will trade bright steel and black coal for fresh produce, but this is just a transaction. Men and dwarves need a deeper understanding of each other so that when war wakes again, they may look to each other for aid. An example of this can be seen in Century Falls, where humans and dwarves have stood shoulder to shoulder (in a manner of speaking) for decades. Only at Century Falls have two races come together and looked beyond their own interests to the future, in an attempt to

4 Khaeris, Star of the West.

serve the welfare of all. Even half-elves, ever Naer Evain's least-wanted children, have begun to make residence within this great and blossoming city. Here perhaps is the hope of a thaw in the frigid relations between dwarf and elf. If we humans are to stand and survive the ravages of orcs and Umber Wraiths, then we will only do so if we stand with the other races, and while no dwarf can yet admit it, they depend on us as much as we depend on them.

Yours faithfully,
Sebastian Venghaus
Anthropologist Royal

The Dwarven Field Manual
Field Notes

Århundrade: century, one hundred years. Also, a
company of one hundred dwarves – although this is a
somewhat misleading title as such a company usually
consists of only sixty to eighty dwarves due to
wounded or retired members.

Berigunn the Furious: king of Voss Kilda and prosecutor
of the Siege of Korlahsia. Father of Killi 'Temper'
Berigunn and Faffnir Berigunn.

bikkja: derogatory term for elf. Also bitch, or dog.

Brutenmakt: the great serpent, Scale King; literally,
'broken tooth'. Oldest and most powerful of all the
Great Drakes, ultimately the creator of the dwarves.
Rumoured to reside near Kourgaad Pass.

Century Falls: dwarven citadel that has become the
melting pot of Naer Evain. Fleeing serfs from the
Arend Kingdoms seek new lives here, as well as half-
elves, who find little solace with the elves or in human
settlements. Century Falls was called Voss Traish
before it seceded from the nascent Union of Dwarven
Peoples.

dvergiir: dwarf in the mother tongue.

Faffnir: revered dwarf ancestor – remembered for

legendary procrastination. Spent a year reorganising his pickaxes.

Faffnir, Berigunn II: successor to Berigunn the Furious of Voss Kilda. He was the second son, and ascended the throne due to his brother being slain by elves at Korlahsia.

folka: dialect word for people.

Forseti: three venerable dwarves that oversee all the legal disputes of any given citadel. They sit on the Ragnvaldr, the ruling council, which provides counsel to the king.

Frosthatar: a Great Drake reported to live in the volcano that overlooks Mourning Point. Frosthatar is deep blue in colour.

ginning: literal translation means deluding, also the dwarf word for magic, specifically elf magic.

gunn: star.

'His beard is longer than it looks': a person wise beyond their years.

hjälm: helmet. Received upon a dwarf's twentieth birthday.

Hojta-dirigent: often just '*Hojta*' or simply '*Hoj*'. A rank above *Striden-dirigent* but below the command rank of *Stridenvaldr*.

huggtand: fangs. This is the name given to a *trupp* using crossbows. They are usually made up of younger dwarves led by a few seasoned veterans.

hulda: hidden.

huldurfolka: known as golems in Nai Roche and as stone giants to the Arends. The *huldurfolka* were created by the dragons to build their great subterranean halls, then discarded when the dragons created the dwarves. They are around thirty feet tall.

Kajsa Storkrona: daughter of the last king of Voss Traish. She decided to rename the citadel Voss Traish as Century Falls one hundred years after the end of the siege of Korlahsia. She is a very divisive historic figure.

Kall Krona: 'cold crown' – a ring made by Brutenmakt. Too large for mortal fingers, it is instead best worn as a crown. It renders the wearer immune to fire. Taken by starving dwarves who were caught and killed for their transgression. Worn by Odniir Dwarf-Father at the start of the rebellion.

Keivan 'Biletongue' Russ: famous on account of his strongly worded opinions and being 'nearly the height of a man'. Historic accounts put him at five feet and speak of his great skill with an axe in each hand.

Killi 'Temper' Berigunn: son of Berigunn the Furious. Killi became lost on a journey to Voss Traish, whereupon he blundered into Korlahsia, burial place of the elves. He refused to lead his expedition away from Korlahsia and was killed by the Watchers of the Dead. This action led to the siege of Korlahsia. It was hoped Killi would marry Kajsa Storkrona and bring the fiercely independent citadel in line with the nascent 'Union of Dwarven Peoples'.

kjol: skirt, specifically *stridenskjol*, which is a skirt made from padded leather.

Kull: equivalent to an earl.

Maskentunga: a Great Drake that lives to the south. Maskentunga means 'wormtongue'; he is so called because he enjoys riddles, and is also known for his deceitfulness.

Menja: a *huldurfolka* living in the White Maw Mountains, creator of the ten auroch belts.

Mittvinterhelg: a holiday celebrated during the middle of winter. Presents are exchanged and dwarves everywhere make a show of gratitude to their ancestors, and Odniir Dwarf-Father in particular.

näven-trupp: 'fist' squad – dwarves that bear hammers in battle. The hammer is often referred to as 'the fist of the dwarves'.

Nedanförvärld: the world beneath. Dwarves believe the mountains are figurative cave walls, and therefore all the world exists in one gigantic cavern. Equivalent of the elf 'Naer Evain'.

nockiir: water serpent, prevalent in mountain rivers and lakes. Known as knucker by the Arends. Frequently reach twenty feet in length, although larger ones have been reported. Able to swallow livestock whole (goats, I suspect, as opposed to cows).

Northern Road, The Great: a trade route across the Kourgaad Plains linking Voss Drun, Voss Kilda and the Scarsfaalen Forest. Voss Traish's (now Century Falls) refusal to share the cost of the road-building contributed to the failure of the Union of Dwarven Peoples.

oathbreaker: the most terrible of insults among dwarves.

Odniir Dwarf-Father: originally known as Odniir Longbeard; leader of the dwarven rebellion, wisest of dwarfs, wearer of the Kall Krona.

odniir-näven: gauntlets. Literally, 'fist of Odniir'.

'Of little beard and little sense': said of the young, and humans.

Osjälviska Storkrona: brother of Kajsa Storkrona.

Osjälviska sought out the Ruiirmaidens who persuaded him to abandon his kingdom. He was never seen again, although some claimed he led a small mercenary company in the years that followed.

oxarnacke: a leather collar covering the neck and shoulders, usually worn beneath armour.

Ragnvaldr: the ruling council in a citadel, typically made up of seven noble-born dwarves and three Forseti. Also, adviser or ruler; a rank held by every dwarf on the Citadel Council.

Rakh Vasskniv: a dwarf inventor who contributed to early designs for the *huldurlantern*. He died while trying to perfect explosive crossbow bolts. To date, no one has followed up on his research.

Rakhyvel: a Great Drake living in the White Maw Mountains. Rakhyvel translates as 'razor sharp'. It was Rakhyvel that created the Huldurfolka Krona, which is kept at Century Falls.

Raseri the Unclean: a Great Drake said to live in a volcano close to the Scarlet Fang Pass. He is a prolific crafter of magical objects and decidedly fragrant.

Renaming, The: when Kajsa Storkrona decided to make Voss Traish a republic and rename it Century Falls. This happened one hundred years after the siege of Korlahsia.

Ruiirmaidens: three female water spirits, elfin in appearance. Many tales surround the maidens, who bewitch and enchant dwarves with their great beauty. They are enigmatic and cryptic, and can foretell dire events. It is said they have skin the colour of milk and waist-length black hair. They are capricious and have been known to drown the weak-willed. Also known as Norns.

Ruszalkai: malevolent water spirits who appear as ghosts. They can take many forms, but are always female. They cast enchantments on themselves and the land to lure the unwary to their deaths. It is said a Ruszalkai can be dispersed if the drowned corpse that spawned it can be given a proper burial.

Sektion-dirigent: equivalent to a corporal. Answers to the *Striden-dirigent* of his *trupp*.

skulda: storyteller and bard. Many dwarf epics are presented as verse, sung in low and sonorous tones. Skulda are not always welcome, often viewed as layabouts and hedonists.

sperasska: outcast dwarves. Literally, 'kicked out'. Sometimes dwarves choose to become outcast, but most are criminals or oathbreakers.

Stor-striden: a rarely used title. Equivalent to General. Dwarven armies are usually led by their kings. A *Stor-striden* is appointed if the king is unable to fight.

Storgunn: known to the elves and humans as Khaeris.

Storvaldr: dwarven king. Ascension to the throne is determined through lineage. The original dwarven kings were the heroes who led the uprising against the Great Drakes, and organised the exodus. The king of Voss Kilda claims to trace his line back to Odniir Dwarf-Father. Voss Traish lost its royal family and has never recognised a new ruling family.

Striden-dirigent: often just 'dirigent', leader of a squad of nineteen dwarves. A sergeant.

Stridenvaldr: literally, 'battle-ruler'. Equivalent to a lieutenant in our own armies.

Sundin Hallestøm: born in Voss Kilda, Sundin spent most of his life as a *Striden-dirigent* but served briefly as a *Stor-striden*. He was demoted and journeyed to fight at Century Falls before returning to Voss Kilda some years later. He is the author of *The Dwarven Field Manual*.

talongen-trupp: talon squad. These dwarves fight using axes.

tomb blights: chitinous spiders the size of a pony. They feed on the dead and set traps for the living. They are expert climbers and have a venomous bite.

trupp: troop, or squad. Usually around twenty dwarves, sometimes divided into two *sektions*.

Union of Dwarven Peoples: an idea that all citadels should cease being independent city states and become one nation, with Voss Kilda as the capital city. While the bonds between dwarves are strong, there are few who are keen to give up their independence, hence the Union has never been adopted in any meaningful way. The Union of Dwarven Peoples was abandoned when Voss Traish formally seceded and renamed itself Century Falls.

vaetiir: the collective name given to all water spirits, but can also include the *huldurfolka*.

vandratrupp: small teams of messengers, typically three to five. Traditionally they travelled between the halls of the dragons, then between dwarven citadels. '*Vanda*' means to wander, or hike.

Vathhrudniir: oldest of all the *huldurfolka*. Reputed to sleep beneath Voss Kilda and will only awaken for a great battle known to all dwarves as the Day of Reckoning.

visundr: a wild mountain bison hunted by the dwarves. Less imposing than the auroch of the plains.

Vodyniir: these loathsome creatures resemble portly old men who appear barefoot. Their feet and hands are webbed, revealing them as water spirits. *Vodyniir* have a deep love of hats, the more flamboyant the better. They can also be identified by their straggly beards, which may contain fish heads or weeds. They are cantankerous and untrustworthy, often trying to drown unwary travellers.

voss: citadel.

Voss Colg: perhaps the least friendly and most socially isolated of the dwarven citadels.

Voss Drun: the dwarves of Voss Drun have trading contracts with the humans of Hoim. They use barges along the Great Southern River (Suinfuen). Drun is also the starting point of the Great Northern Road, which stretched across the Kourgaad Plains to the Kingdom of Arendsonn.

Voss Jur: a citadel most famous for the quality of its warriors. The dwarves of Voss Jur are of a particularly sour disposition but save the greater part of their vehemence for elves.

Voss Kilda: the largest and oldest of the dwarf citadels, although partly in ruins. The Great Breach occurred in the Time of Tears, when a horde of goblins attacked. Voss Kilda is also afflicted by tomb blights. Voss Kilda has trading contracts with both Hoim and the Kingdom of Arendsonn.

Voss Traish: a dwarf citadel to the north of the Kourgaad Plains. See Century Falls.